ALICE *In* ACADEME

And Other Stories

Joe Wessling

Professor Emeritus of English
Xavier University

Illustrations
Holly Schapker

Creative Direction, Book Design, Graphic
Illustration and Digital Prepress
Margaret Walker

Library of Congress Cataloging-in-Publication Data

Wessling, Joseph H.
ISBN 0-9769595-0-X
1. Satire-Academic 2. *Alice In Wonderland* 3. Literary Criticism
4. Education 5. Fantasy 6. Graduate Studies

Printed in the United States of America
Published by RLT Communications, Inc.

Dedicated to
Adelaide and John

Acknowledgements

The Annotated Alice, containing *Alice's Adventures In Wonderland* and *Through The Looking Glass* by Lewis Carroll. Ed. and annotated by Martin Gardner. New York: Bramhall House, 1960. Conveniently used for Lewis Carroll references.

"A Very Fishy Story" first appeared in *The Kenyon Review*, New Series. XI (Winter 1989) 36-39.

"Narrative Epistolary, Referee A Bit Contrary, Novice Poet Quite Unwary" first appeared in *Thalia: Studies In Literary Humor*. XI (Fall and Winter 1990) 41-42.

"The Last Shall Be First" first appeared in *Thalia: Studies In Literary Humor*. XV (1995) 90-93.

The quote from Benjamin Lehmann in the Preface may be found in "Comedy and Laughter," University of California Publications, English Studies. Vol 10 (1954) 81-101.

Preface

When I first conceived of this book in 1991, I had in mind a collection of sketches to be entitled "Literary Theory Meets the Satiric Muse." But, as the book evolved, the satiric element became integrated into a larger, comic vision. Satire is essentially negative and therefore an incomplete view of almost anything save the atrocious and the inane. For that reason, and because of my chronic, irrational optimism, I found a celebratory element creeping into my stories willy-nilly. The Comic Muse had displaced the Satiric Muse — irreversibly so. I changed my title tentatively to "The Comic Muse in Academe."

Also, it had occurred to me that, since contemporary academe is in many ways a wonderland (especially in the humanities), Lewis Carroll's Alice — reappearing as a graduate student in English — might be the perfect protagonist for one of my stories. By the time I had completed "A New Kind of Wonderland," I realized that there were countless possibilities for Alice in this academic wonderland, and before long I had taken her through ten episodes. The temptation was to exploit more and more possibilities, increasing the episodes to twenty or thirty. But sufficient for one graduate program are the absurdities — and the joys — thereof. I resolved to stop at ten, but already Alice, as she had done a century ago, had earned top billing: *"Alice in Academe" and Other Stories.* Lewis Carroll, wherever you are, did it occur to you that you might be metamorphosed so posthumously into an avatar of the Comic Muse, whom you served so brilliantly in life? May you be pleased with your Alice's progress and not saddened to see her grow up. She is ever so grateful that Wonderland and the other side of that looking-glass were such suitable preparations for the world of academe.

It is right that academe should be a wonderland. In one sense, it always has been, for it involves an exploration of all that is awesome in the physical universe, in art, and in the many visions of the transcendent by which we reach out for order and meaning amid the fragmentation and transitoriness in which we seem to be immersed. But "wonderland" can also designate a world of absurdities, such as academe has in many respects become. Today, one of the great buzzwords in the humanities is "demystification," a term born of the idolatry of reason, so pervasive in contemporary academe. It is a term rarely heard from our colleagues in physics, chemistry and biology, who know that deep probings of the physical world do not dispel mystery but reveal greater cause for wonder. In the humanities, such awe has become an embarrassment, but why? The volumes that have been written on the character of Hamlet have made him, not less of a mystery, but a deeper mystery.

We live in an age of "theory." Now there is nothing wrong with theory; it is as old as Aristotle, and as new as any yesterday. But too many humanists, unlike the scientists, fail to put theory into perspective. Today's theorists, like the more extreme neoclassical critics, tend to be absolutists, and the victims of their rational constructs are often reality and common sense (a term which my long departed colleague Bob Lavelle defined as "the ability to see the obvious"). Every theory is reductive and has a limited range of relevance. "What are the limitations of your theory?" The theorist who can answer that question is a sound theorist, but it is as welcome a question as "How will you reduce the deficit?"

Perhaps no one has seen more clearly the limitations of reason than Benjamin Lehmann, who in "Comedy and Laughter" rejected the notion that reason is at the heart of the comic vision, calling that notion "a snobbery of the self-valuing intelligence." Lehmann's full critique is worth reading, though I must gloss over it here. He comes to this conclusion: "Reason is not the instrument of comic vision. It is part of the material upon which the comic vision gazes." Reason, like humans, becomes comic when it makes a pretense which reality does not support. Lehmann (probably with full awareness) put his finger on why the comic spirit finds its usual outlet in the imagination.

George Meredith, amid the great intellectual activity of the second half of the nineteenth century, lamented the absence of the comic genius in his day. Fortunately Wilde and Shaw were just beyond the horizon, and Twain was already at work in America. Today, comic geniuses abound, exploiting especially the worlds of politics and entertainment, but few thus far have cast a penetrating gaze on the fertile field of academe, David Lodge being one of the more notable exceptions. My book is intended as a small contribution to what is as yet a small scale campaign to restore common sense to the upper echelons of academe. I know that Folly is as hard to kill as the Hydra. But Folly, unlike the Hydra, may be enjoyed while it lives, and, if the stories in this book prove no more than an aid to that enjoyment, the effort will have been worthwhile.

I wish to thank Don Wigal, Karl Wentersdorf, Wes Vordenberg,

Joe Dussourd, Alison Young Homann, Roz Gann, Vytas Bieliauskas, Teresa Sowers, my wife Adelaide, and especially my son John, for their valuable suggestions and support. Thanks especially are due to the English Department secretary Linda Loomis for her virtually flawless work in the preparation of the typescript. I am sincerely grateful to Holly Schapker whose illustrations have enriched the book, catching its spirit and gracing it with her own genius. Special thanks are due to Margaret Walker whose remarkable technical skills and artistic vision are evident on the cover and on every page.

Finally, I must express my gratitude to those many luminaries of the academic firmament who have provided the comic muse with such irresistible material.

Joe Wessling
Xavier University

ALICE *In* ACADEME

And Other Stories

"When I used to read fairy tales, I fancied that kind of thing never happened, and now here I am in the middle of one! There ought to be a book written about me, that there ought!..."

–The Annotated Alice, p. 59

Contents

Alice & Hugh On The Wall

"*Don't you think you'd be safer down on the ground?*"
Alice went on, not with any idea of making another riddle,
but simply in her good natured anxiety for the queer creature.

—The Annotated Alice, p. 263

A New Kind of Wonderland

*A*lice was not surprised to find herself walking across the campus of a large American university, Parnassus by name, about to begin graduate studies in English. She knew that Lewis Carroll had bestowed immortality upon her; besides, she had experienced much stranger things than immortality. Of course, she was surprised that someone over a hundred years old could look and feel as young as she. But some things, like youth, are better enjoyed than questioned. (There is a time for all things under the sun, including the unexamined life.) So Alice just let herself be enchanted by the beauty around her: mature trees, flowering shrubs, expanses of wildflowers, and those ivy-clad buildings where nature meets tradition in an intimate embrace. She passed an aged, sprawling live oak and thought, "That's what Shakespeare would have been had he been a tree." She stopped to admire a graceful weeping willow, just the sort of tree Petrarch would have planted had he been a gardener. She paused on a quaint wooden bridge and looked down upon a clear stream, flowing past grassy banks and water fowl toward where the sun would set, thinking "west-running brook." "How my imagination is coloring my experience today!" murmured Alice and she looked at her face in the water, half expecting to see the features of Wordsworth. But she saw the features of Alice, looking perhaps twelve years older than those shown to the world in 1865.

"How my imagination is coloring my experience today!" murmured Alice.

"How neat and orderly," exclaimed Alice.

As Alice walked on, she gradually realized that she was not imagining things—that the trees, the flowers, the stream, the wildlife—everything about her—had an imagination of its own, that her mind and spirit were themselves being colored by a nature already transformed.

I could go on like this forever, thought Alice. Whereupon a sad but kindly voice floated down, "No, you can't!" Startled, she raised her eyes to see not twenty feet away a high stone wall, and, sitting atop the wall, a young man whose rounded torso gave her a sense of deja vu.

"Do you read minds?"

"I read faces. They're much like computer screens. On yours I read an impossible dream, such as this landscape calls up. You're the new graduate student."

"Yes. I'm Alice."

"Hugh Dumphrey, Assistant Professor of English. Like to share the wall with me? There are stone steps just past that flower in the cranny."

So Alice joined Dr. Dumphrey on the wall and was shocked at the contrast between the two terrains which the wall divided. The ground she had passed through seemed like a formal garden. Broad avenues, lines of trees, footpaths and rows of buildings divided the landscape into triangles, squares, ovals, and other recognizable shapes.

"How neat and orderly," exclaimed Alice.

"Like a table of contents—or a syllabus for a survey course."

"I was just walking there," mused Alice, "and it seemed so different—so alive, so rich and varied, so full of surprises."

"So it is if you immerse yourself in it."

"I saw a live oak that I almost took for Shakespeare."

"Very likely it was."

"And a weeping willow that I fancied had been planted by Petrarch."

"Yes, indeed. He had everyone planting them for a while."

"The terrain seemed so different when I was down there," repeated Alice.

"Now you have an academic view—much neater, don't you think?"

"If neatness is what one prefers,—"

"Some don't," interrupted Dumphrey. "They prefer the other side of the wall." Alice found the other side not at all to her liking—Escher-like buildings and a grey tangle of some of the strangest vegetation she had ever seen. Not a path could be discerned, hardly a splash of color anywhere. "Postmodernism," explained Dumphrey. "There's a fair amount of literary output there, and an enormous quantity of theory."

"But it's all so dense and tangled," protested Alice. "Theory is an attempt to clarify and to order."

"Stop, stop! You'll crack me up." Dumphrey seemed genuinely alarmed at being moved to laughter. Alice fell silent, and her wall-sitting companion sensed that she was concerned and intimidated, so he soon resumed the conversation. "Theory now claims the title 'literature' on an equal footing with works of imagination. If the latter may be obscure, involved, and fantastic, may not theory be equally so? You are looking upon the new frontier in literary studies, the field of

> "*Theory is an attempt to clarify and order.*"

"Then the wall is...?"

academic stardom, where reputations and fortunes are made. 'One must go in to fetch a diamond out.' Academia has its Uncle Bens, you know--also its Aunt Benitas." The last phrase seemed hurriedly and nervously added.

"Fortunes are to be made by sorting out that tangle?"

"Or by further tangling it—that is how the greatest fame is achieved."

"Have you made your fortune yet?" inquired Alice.

"Heavens no. I'll settle for tenure. That's why I'm on this wall."

"So you're a modernist."

"No, no, no." Dumphrey seemed again alarmed, though he was not laughing.

"But if we are between the ground of tradition and postmodernism, this wall must be modernism."

Alice was confident of the logic of her position, but Dumphrey pointed to the grey tangle and proclaimed, "Modernism is out there too. Postmodernism grew out of it and over it, so that it is largely obscured, but, to the trained eye, the monuments of modernism can be discerned. Do you see that phallic structure, something like the Washington Monument, almost obscured by vines?"

"Something like a utility pole enveloped by kudzu?"

"Hemingway in the grip of feminist criticism. To the right is Yeats, the mosaic tower with the golden bird above it like an elegant weather cock--too tall and shining to be completely obscured. Ezra Pound is there somewhere, self-obscured, mostly."

"Then the wall is...?"

"The *via media*, and, for those who tread it carefully, the road to tenure…or a Ph.D."

"But isn't it a dangerous road? It's narrow, even a bit slippery, and some twenty feet high. You could have a great fall," remarked Alice, suspecting herself of plagiarism.

"If I fell from the ground, I could fall a great deal farther, let me tell you. I could fall into non-renewal."

"Is that so very far?"

"It's a hole some never get out of." Dumphrey had broken into a sweat just thinking about it. "The trick is to offend neither the traditionalists nor the postmodernists. It's a balancing act, and some do fall, but it's still the safest way. There are magic words to get you out of any difficulty: 'On the one hand…on the other hand.' Coming along?"

"Yes," said Alice, but with hesitation in her voice. "Oh, I do hate to leave Shakespeare behind."

"But you won't. No matter how far you walk, he'll be no more distant than now. Once you have found shelter in his shade, scaled his heights, or sat among his turning leaves, he is beside you forever."

And so Alice walked the wall with Dr. Dumphrey. Not beside him—he was too wide and the wall too narrow for that. She lagged behind him, or sometimes slipped by him and raced ahead as she gained confidence. Beside her walked others--Shakespeare, Virginia Woolf, Emily Dickinson—delightful companions, who took up very little room, only the width of a book. Alice was not at all puzzled that they could be simultaneously on the ground below and on the wall with her, or that they could be where she was, where

"The via media, and for those who tread it carefully, the road to tenure…or a Ph.D."

"You can make it, girl,..."

she had been, and waiting for her where she was going. She was especially grateful for their presence on those stormy days when the thunders of the deconstructionists were answered by the bellows of the traditionalists, and Alice found herself buffetted from both sides. "Still better than the ground," maintained Dumphrey. "Down there we could get swallowed up." He watched the dark clouds gathering. "Dry sterile thunder and no rain. Both the thunders and the bellows will eventually subside into the obscurity of footnotes," he forecast.

"They'll not go gently into that good night," replied Alice. Dumphrey's smile of admiration mirrored her own inward smile of self-approval. "You can make it, girl," she told herself as she wondered what other storms and marvels lay ahead on the stony road she would coambulate with Dr. Dumphrey.

Dr. Corona

"*How she longed to get out of that dark hall and wander about those beds of bright flowers and those cool fountains, but she could not even get her head through the doorway...*"
—The Annotated Alice, p. 207

A Little Help From Her Friends

"Nothing personal... Time is publications."

"You want to see Professor Corona before you register, but she won't want to see you." The speaker was Janet, a gangly young graduate student, well over six feet tall with an unusually long neck. Alice, who after a century still retained her vivid memories of her own transformation in Wonderland, had felt an immediate kinship upon meeting her.

"Not want to see me? Why ever not?" asked Alice, who had been welcomed everywhere else on campus.

"Nothing personal. She's very busy, you know. Time is publications."

Time obsessed? Alice recalled the Rabbit who was always scurrying about and checking his watch. Was Professor Corona like that? It seemed not. "Active hibernation" was the phrase used by Janet, who was planning a dissertation on oxymorons. "But you must visit her den before registering for courses."

The word "den" conjured up unnerving images, associated in Alice's mind with bears and even a Cyclops. "Foolish fears" Alice chided herself. "Images most unprofessional." So Alice had braced herself and set off for the den of Rosa Corona, somewhere in the bowels of the main library, a building larger by far than the largest manor house Alice had ever seen. Lewis Carroll had prepared her for strange encounters but not for what was to follow.

"I almost feel I'm back in Wonderland, but this is different. It's..."

Upon entering, Alice stated her mission to the security guard, who made it sound simple. "Room 210 off the second floor of the stacks." But at the entrance to the stacks was a student guard who needed to see the pass she did not have. No pass no entry, but "no problem," really. He referred her to the Information Desk, where the information was that she would have to get a pass. But where? She might "try the Director's Office."

Which she did. The Director was not in. The Director's assistant was sympathetic, but bound by the rules. A pass was required to enter the stacks. "I can issue one, if you have a registration form signed by Dr. Corona."

"But I must go through the stacks to see Dr. Corona."

"That does make it difficult."

"Impossible," corrected Alice.

"Yes, it's a Catch 22, isn't it?" Alice did not know what a Catch 22 was, but she remembered audibly "it takes all the running you can do to keep in the same place."

"The White Queen!" The Director's assistant perked up. "You're Alice from Wonderland! I should have recognized you."

Alice was becoming a "celebrity," Hugh had told her. Now she was experiencing that mixed blessing. It did not relieve her frustration. "I almost feel I'm back in Wonderland, but this is different. It's ..."

"Bureaucracy. Ain't it awful?" If sympathy could have opened doors for Alice she would have left with a master key. But she did get something. Her celebrity status kicked in. "Listen. I'm not supposed to do this, but I'm giving you a one-day pass to the stacks. Just don't tell anyone."

Armed with her pass Alice headed for the entrance to the stacks, where in place of the guard she found a sign: RETURN SOON. So she proceeded through the unlocked door with her unneeded pass and headed for the promised land, the square occupied by Queen Corona. But first there would be forty minutes of wandering in the desert, otherwise known as the stacks. Alice felt guilty about mixing her metaphors but more so about thinking of the stacks as desert. She had read John Keats: "Much have I traveled in the realms of gold." An avid reader, she had experienced the truth of that metaphor. Books could be golden — on the inside. But Alice had no time for reading now, and books on the outside could be drab and uninviting. Here were such books by the thousands imprisoned in dark grey steel shelving with not a liberator in sight.

Alice began to wander this dry, dusty sameness in search of an elevator and was heartened by a sign at the corner of the building:

ELEVATOR ⏩

Taking the direction of the arrow, Alice walked the length of the building without seeing an elevator. What she did see at the other end of the dimly lighted corridor was another sign:

⏪ ELEVATOR

I must have passed it, thought Alice, but I watched so carefully. So she retraced her steps past double rows of books with carrels visible at the other ends of the narrow aisles, silhouetted against dusty windows.

...there would be forty minutes of wandering in the desert...

"but...

I climbed

only two

flights

of stairs."

The long line of stacks was interrupted only by a short stretch of plain brick wall, and Alice soon found herself back at

ELEVATOR ⯮

Looking back, toward and beyond the entrance to the stacks, Alice noticed a lighted sign:

EXIT

She was not ready to exit, but she knew that such a sign often appears outside a stairwell, and she made her way down another long, long corridor. Sure enough, there were stairs going up and stairs going down. The second floor obviously would be up, so Alice climbed two flights of stairs (it seems that in the stacks there are floors between the floors), and entered a door bearing a single numeral: 6. "But I can't be on the sixth floor, I climbed only two flights of stairs." (She was thinking aloud now.) "Perhaps the '6' is a code number of some kind."

Just then, from somewhere in the distance, Alice heard a cough. Off she went, past ELEVATOR, past dark grey, dusty stacks, past a short blank wall, past more stacks, and was about to pass ELEVATOR when she heard a page rustle. At a carrel by the window, she found the source of the cough and the rustle, an elderly gentleman, who introduced himself as John Blather and greeted her warmly. Wouldn't she sit down? Have a bit of a chat? Alice had to decline. She explained her errand. "Yes, yes," replied Blather, "you must see Dr. Corona. She's your director. But she's not on this floor."

"She's on the second," said Alice.

"You're on the sixth," advised Blather.

"How can that be," asked Alice. "I'm one floor above the entrance."

"Above the High Street entrance. The library's built into a hillside, you know. You'll have to take the elevator down to "2.""

"If I can find the elevator."

"You just passed it, half way down the corridor."

"I saw a blank wall."

"The back of the elevator shaft. The doors face away from the corridor.

Alice thanked her mentor and scurried off looking at her watch. "I'm becoming the Rabbit," she thought, then tried to put that disturbing thought out of her mind.

But she did find the elevator and she did find the second floor, and after exactly forty minutes of "wandering in the desert" she stood before a formidable oak door with a brass plate bearing the designation "Rosa Corona, Ph.D." Below the name was a card reading

> ### OFFICE HOURS
> Wednesdays 9:00-10:00 a.m.

Alice wondered at the plural "HOURS," but only for a moment. She checked her watch Rabbit-like and saw that it was 10:08. "Oh dear, oh dear!" Alice caught herself. "Now I'm *sounding* like the

"I'm becoming the rabbit," she thought.

Finally, however, Alice's advisor reluctantly began to give advice.

Rabbit! Oh dear! I mean, oh no." At least, it was Wednesday. She was determined to knock no matter what the hour and waited just a minute only to catch her breath. Then she knocked.

The voice from beyond the door had a ring of authority: "Come in, Marjorie." Alice was hesitant to enter, her name not being Marjorie, but the voice repeated "Come in," this time commandingly without the "Marjorie," so Alice made bold to enter. "Marjorie, I want you to . . . you're not Marjorie."

"No. I'm Alice."

"I was expecting my research assistant. Don't tell me you've been sent to replace Marjorie."

"No, Dr. Corona. I'm come about my course registration."

It was Dr. Corona's turn to look at her watch. "You're late. My office hours are over for the day."

"For the week." Alice was surprised by her boldness.

"Yes. For the week," agreed Dr. Corona impassively. "Oh, give me your registration form, and I'll sign it."

"But I've not filled out a registration form. I don't know what courses to take."

Impassivity yielded to impatience. Alice should know the requirements of her program. She had in hand the course offerings. There was no excuse for coming unprepared. Etc., etc., etc. Finally, however, Alice's advisor reluctantly began to give advice. She must take Research in English. Among other possibilities, Dr. Corona strongly recommended The Ancients and the Moderns offered by Dr. Jerry Trigger, etc., etc. Within a very few minutes, Alice had in hand a signed registration form and was headed out the door.

"Thank you, Your Maj__ . . . er . . . . Thank you, Dr. Corona." But the hibernating scholar seemed not to hear. Already she was squinting at her computer screen, transported into cyberspace at the touch of a key. Alice took time to size her up: the broad shoulders and hips, the muscular arms and legs, the wild reddish hair that fitted her head like a shaggy helmet. "More like Brunnhilde than the White Queen," noted Alice. "But, really, I must stop connecting real people with fictions. Some day I'll thoughtlessly offend someone." Alice was possessed of a lively analogical imagination, though she had yet to learn that term. "Brunnhilde," mused Alice, now outside the closed oak door. "She may not be hibernating within a ring of fire, but that oak door serves her well enough."

Alice made her way to the elevator and pushed the DOWN button. "I'll exit on the lower level," she said to herself. Perhaps there'll be a garden there." And there was.

"More like Brunnhilde than the White Queen," noted Alice.

Blather At The Harpsichord

The Red Queen shook her head. **"***You may call it nonsense if you like,***"** *she said,* **"***but* I've *heard nonsense compared with which that would be as sensible as a dictionary!***"**

—The Annotated Alice, p. 207

The House Of Blather

...a call to enter a by-gone age and become part of it.

$\mathcal{B}$oth the demands of graduate study and those of the human spirit called Alice down from the wall more often than was thought safe by Hugh Dumphrey, who kept such excursions to a minimum and urged the inexperienced student to do the same. Replied the more adventurous Alice, "The wall is my refuge; I shall not fear."

Her favorite excursion was to the home of John Blather, nearly the oldest professor on campus, famous throughout the humanities departments and beyond for his intimate dinner parties. An invitation to John Blather's century-old Tudor residence was a call to enter a bygone age and become part of it. Classical music melodied the premises, and the interior was adorned with reminders of the Western heritage: a facsimile page of the Gutenberg Bible, a bust of Shakespeare, a portrait of Keats, and the only harpsichord on campus, which the host always played for his guests once they promised to join him in singing "Greensleeves." Blather himself was representative to the point of caricature of the gentleman scholar. He was tall, thin, a bit stooped, and always wore dress slacks, tweed coat, and a conservative tie. "I can remember," he once told Alice in his high-toned Anglicized accent, "when the students were dressed much like me. And, when they completed their four years, they thought like me. There was real education in those days."

Blather's one notable departure from tradition was his insistence

"I prefer my literature rare, like my steaks."

on informal relationships. He disdained the titles of "Doctor" and "Professor." "John Blather. Call me John — Blather if you'd rather." He had addressed those very words to hundreds (thousands? wondered Alice) of new acquaintances, followed by a presumably identical chuckle. It was his lead-in for a reminiscence about his Oxford days when everyone — tutors and schoolmates alike — addressed him as Blather. "There were many Johns at Oxford, as you can imagine, but only one Blather. I liked the uniqueness of it — still do!" He would tell of the tutor's response to his first academic effort: "'Lovely paper, Blather, pity you had nothing to say.' Had me there he did. Taught me a lot that chap." And he would recreate his past with such charm that to tire of an oft repeated reminiscence was to tire of a virtuoso performance.

What did Blather know of contemporary literary theory? "Not much, old chap," he was likely to respond. "I prefer my literature rare, like my steaks. They cook the flavor out of things these days. Ever read that piece by Hillis Miller on 'A Slumber Did My Spirit Seal'? He not only overcooks it, he chews on it for ten pages. Not very appetizing after that, what?" Indeed, Blather's knowledge of contemporary theory was superficial and destined to remain so. A younger colleague so little read in the latest twists and turns of textual scrutinies would have been defenseless among the aficionados of Paul de Man and Roland Barthes. But Blather had his defenses: an old-world charm, a nimble wit, and an astounding erudition in non-contemporary literature. He would listen for a while with apparent interest to jargon-laden, name-dropping exchanges before interjecting an appropriate literary quote and adding "You recognize that, of course," suspecting that they would not. When no one could place it, he would continue, "Never read Traherne (or Landor or Alexander Smith)? Pity. Not too late you know." And he would saunter off, satisfied that he had effected another checkmate.

But Blather's best defense was an ability to laugh at himself, reflected in the only contemporary art anywhere in his home: a framed cartoon from the student newspaper. The caricatured countenance of John Blather had been mounted upon the neck of a prehistoric reptile in a museum setting, behind a sign reading

> BLATHERSAURUS
> thought to be extinct
> until one was discovered
> in the twentieth century

No guest was allowed to overlook it. "Good likeness, what? Walter Thomas had the cheek to say that the cartoonist made the head too small but had gotten the rest of me right." His was the self-deprecating banter of the self-confident.

As one should imagine, Alice's first attendance at a Blather gathering was fascinating and agreeable. She never felt at home on the wall (who would?) and certainly not on the post-modern side of it. The ground of tradition was much to her liking, and the Blather residence was almost home to the late Victorian lass. Alice and the old traditionalist shared literary tastes, Oxford memories, and a respect for the social graces. The old man (who was technically younger than Alice) knew better than she what had gone on in Wonderland

She never felt at home on the wall... certainly not the post-modern side of it.

In white velvet and a glittering crown, Blather made a splendid White King.

and on the other side of the looking-glass, having read the annotated edition. How doubly marvelous it was to relive those experiences with Blather as tour guide, and how sad it was when that first visit had to come to an end.

"What a lovely evening, Hugh," Alice was still saying several days later.

"You're almost as repetitious as Blather, Alice. Good thing you're twice as charming."

Then something happened to raise Alice's spirits even higher: a messenger in the guise of the Mad Hatter delivered to both of them an invitation to a costume party to be held on October 31st at the home of John Blather. Scribbled across the bottom were the commands, "Alice, come as yourself" and "Hugh, I'll outfit you upon arrival." It wasn't hard to guess that Alice's adventures would be the theme of the party, but that only increased the suspense. Who was Hugh to be? Hugh was sure he'd be Humpty Dumpty; Alice wasn't sure.

The big night finally arrived, and the large door of the Blather residence was opened by the Mad Hatter-messenger, who rushed them in and rushed off muttering to himself. "He hasn't changed much," noted Alice.

"Happy birthday, my dear!" She and Hugh found themselves confronted by Blather, who had changed *very* much. In white velvet and a glittering crown, Blather made a splendid White King. His greeting was echoed almost immediately by a female voice behind Alice. She turned to see the White Queen (a.k.a., Joan Blather) in splendor equal to her mate's.

Alice could only stammer in confusion. "But my birth date is a mystery complicated by uncertainties."

"Nonsense," replied the Queen, "it's on the calendar."

"What calendar?"

"Any calendar. Calendars have whatever meaning I create for them. Read Stanley Fish."

Alice turned to share a laugh with Hugh, who was not to be seen. His mysterious disappearance blended in with the familiar strangeness about her, and soon Hugh was out-of-mind amid a frenzy of well wishes from a Queen of Hearts, a Mock Turtle, a Cheshire-Cat, and so many other reminders of old times. The frenzy had not subsided when the tyrannical tones of the Queen of Hearts rose above all others: "Off with their shells!" And there behind an oyster bar stood Hugh, looking as much like the Walrus as a human being can be made to look. Looking also as ill at ease as a human being can look, thought Alice, but she had to laugh. "This is your big break, Hugh. You don't want to be stereotyped as a wall-sitter."

The evening sped by as merrily as evenings do when the company is lively and agreeable. Alice met delightful new acquaintances but wondered how she would recognize them when they were no longer Tweedledum or the Dormouse or whoever. Alice was thinking it was just the middle of the evening when Hugh called her attention to the lateness of the hour, and they went to take leave of their hosts. "The time has come, the Walrus said," explained Alice.

"To sing!" Blather completed the sentence for her, and the royal couple in white made their way to the harpsichord. The White King took his place at the keyboard and his Queen announced that

"This is your big break, Hugh, You don't want to be stereotyped as a wall-sitter."

"I was born...from an inkwell instead of a womb..."

a song had been composed in honor of Alice and that no one was to leave without hearing it. Blather began to play a tune recognized only by Alice, but the words, sung as a dialogue by the host couple, had a familiar ring for many.

"You are old, Mistress Alice," she heard Blather call,
"You're a hundred and thirty, I'd say;
Yet you skip and you leap on a tall stony wall.
Tell me how do you do it, I pray?"

"I was born," Mistress Alice replied to the sage,
"From an inkwell instead of a womb;
And the genuine blue blood that keeps me from age
Gives immunity e'en from the tomb."

"You are old," he repeated, "the mystery unfold,
For your skin has a marvelous glow;
And your hair should be white instead of bright gold—
Unless you'd died ages ago."

"My birthplace was Oxford; my home it is still;
Where only the wine knows to age.
Of antiquities vibrant the dons drink their fill
From a gold, not a yellowing page."

"But you're not now in Oxford," old Blather replied.
"Here the newest cannot long stay new.
Unplanned obsolescence each freshness derides,
So who'd make exception for you?"

"Each year on my birthday, that man Willard Scott
Makes exception for Alice, my friend.
'This is one pretty lady here, folks, is she not?'
So let this discussion now end."

The song was such a hit that two encores were demanded, and at least a half dozen copies were promised before the guests began their frequently delayed departures.

Of the many visits Alice was to make to the house of Blather, this remained her favorite. "Oh, Hugh, don't you wish you could repeat that evening?"

"If I could be myself and you could be the Walrus."

"What kind of Walrus would I make, Hugh? You might as well ask Arnold Schwarzenegger to come as the Dormouse. And it wouldn't do for you to be yourself. The whole idea of a costume party is to put your own reality aside — to fictionalize yourself. I'm already a fiction, so I don't need to be the Walrus or something else."

Alice had won the argument; Hugh was getting used to that.

"I'm already a fiction…"

Treadway & Hearthstone

And they repeated their arguments
to her, though, as they all spoke
at once, she found it very
hard to make out exactly
what they said.

—The Annotated Alice, p. 116

The Ancients And The Moderns

*J*erry Trigger's classes were as dramatic as life itself. He was committed without reservation to the pedagogy of Gerald Graff, who, having observed that we live in a world of conflict and that education is preparation for life, favored the introduction of conflict into the classroom. So Dr. Trigger's classroom was known for heated and polarized exchanges between guest panelists.

The mention of Gerald Graff requires explanation, for he has little to do with Alice or with any kind of Wonderland, but Alice is a fair-minded gentlewoman from the land of cricket. She would be quick (though gentle) with a reprimand were the teller of this tale to leave any room for suspicion that Dr. Trigger's pedagogy was inspired by Jerry Springer, however great the surface similarity. No, Jerry Trigger was into education, not entertainment. Not that you could prove it from the student evaluations. "What did you value most in the course?"

"Seeing Professor Oldman make an ass of himself."

"It was a blast."

"When Dr. Barger said to Dr. Richter, 'Understand me, gray-beard loon.'"

But a professor cannot control student responses any more than the students can. If students found his course entertaining, perhaps they did not find it only entertaining. Alice hoped it might be so. Dr. Trigger did have much to offer. His background in linguistics

"What did you value most in the course?"

"Seeing Professor Oldman make an ass of himself."

"Facts play a supporting role. Logic is a bit player."

had given him a realization of the power of words. He emphasized to students that vocabulary frames arguments and wins them. "Argumentation is the game of the name. Facts play a supporting role. Logic is a bit player." If a student remembers nothing else from a Trigger course, he remembers that.

By the end of the course, Alice would remember that and much more. She saw quickly that, in giving his course the title The Ancients and the Moderns, Dr. Trigger was playing the game of the name. Who wouldn't prefer to be modern, no matter what that meant? And "ancients" to Alice had always denoted the Greeks and Romans and Hebrews of two thousand or more years ago. Such ancients were deserving of respect, thought Alice. "There is grandeur in extreme old age," Koko had sung in that wonderful *Mikado*. But what if the old age were not extreme? Now Shakespeare was deemed an ancient, as were Milton and Pope and even Wordsworth and Keats, and not always with respect. Just old age without the grandeur? It was in The Ancients and the Moderns that Alice first heard the term "dead white males." No ring of grandeur in that. Here was the game of the name. "Dead" was a factual adjective but more than that. It had a ring of dismissal. "Males" seemed to emphasize genitalia where intellectual and aesthetic values were at stake. And "white" would have been neutral enough if it were not in the middle of that linguistic sandwich. "Words are chameleon-like," thought Alice, who was a bit of a poet. "They can take on the coloring of their surroundings." By the end of the semester, Alice would have more insight into the uses and abuses of language than even Dr. Trigger. Lewis Carroll had prepared her well.

Alice was telling Hugh Dumphrey about her early experiences in The Ancients and the Moderns. Dr. Trigger relied heavily on guest speakers to present "both sides" of whatever the issue might be: populism vs. elitism, tradition vs. postmodernism — the possibilities were endless. Most were topics on which Alice would like to be enlightened, and she originally expected a civilized, nuanced exchange which recognized the complexity of the issue. The fulfillment of this expectation was as rare as rain on the Sahara. Typically, the "two sides" each thought there was only one side. And civility often was lost to what one or both speakers must have thought was a higher value (truth? victory? gender loyalty?). There were interruptions, sarcasms, ad hominems, and even (rarely) an angry storming out. Dr. Trigger's most glaring defect as a teacher (as Alice came to realize) was that he valued conflict for its own sake. The classes he deemed most successful were those in which the most sparks flew.

"*Crossfire* comes to Academe," mused Hugh. Alice knew nothing of *Crossfire*. "Let's watch it," suggested Hugh, and so they did. There were Paul Begala on one side, Pat Buchanan on the other, and two polarized guests in the middle (an oxymoron later to be recorded in Janet's notebook). Alice was fascinated. "It's the verbal equivalent of tag wrestling," she observed. (Alice had by this time watched some television, and her analogical imagination was getting sharper.)

Of all the exchanges arranged by Dr. Trigger that semester, the most memorable was that between the noted Arnold scholar, Harold Hearthstone, and the up-and-coming feminist, Millicent Treadway, a champion of Caryll Churchill. The usually cheerful Hearthstone

"It's the verbal equivalent of tag wrestling," she observed.

Hearthstone ...chose to focus on Matthew Arnold..."

was more of a visible than an audible man on campus. Soft spoken and spare of speech, he was known for his tasteful bow ties worn with a white shirt and well coordinated jacket and trousers. He was a walking personification of "the grand style simple."

Dr. Treadway's long pale face was framed by straight, shoulder-length, prematurely graying hair, and her garb was just as plain: a dark, almost black gown, high collared and ankle length. She managed to look elegant, grandmotherly, and nun-like at the same time. "The grand style severe," thought Alice, who had a nodding acquaintance with literary criticism.

"What an odd pair!" thought Alice. "He's certainly older than she, but, given their dress and their demeanors, they might be taken for mother and son!" Their verbal exchanges tended to accentuate this impression. The traditionalist Hearthstone was rebuked from time to time as though he were a young upstart by the motherly corrections of Treadway.

Hearthstone, not surprisingly, chose to focus on Matthew Arnold in his defense of the "Ancients." Alice found it hard to think of Dr. Arnold as an Ancient. Why, she had met him. Not in the flesh, of course. But he had been a frequent visitor in Alice's home — that is to say, in the mind of Lewis Carroll, of whom he was a contemporary.

Hearthstone began with an enthusiastic presentation of "Dover Beach," a prophetic utterance "foreshadowing the Modernist movement." Hearthstone walked the students patiently through the poem, savoring the visual imagery of the first section and the auditory imagery of the second. He pointed out how in its free form the poem may be compared most favorably to the verse of Arnold's contemporary Walt Whitman and how thematically it anticipated *The Waste Land.* In its breadth of vision, Hearthstone averred, "Dover Beach" links the ancient world with the modern: "Sophocles heard it long ago on the Aegean." That "eternal note of sadness" informs the *Antigone* and the *Oedipus Rex* as it informs "Dover Beach" and subsequently *The Return of the Native* and *Waiting for Godot.* But Arnold knew that sadness need not include despair: "Ah, love, let us be true to one another." Love is the other eternal note — a note with which despair cannot contend. Beckett's Di Di and Go Go never quite despair. Because they have love, they have hope and the lone tree on their desolate landscale breaks out in leaves. In short, (Hearthstone became uncharacteristically dramatic in his conclusion) Matthew Arnold's vision is an eternal vision. Neither an ancient nor a modern, he is the prophet who past and future sees — a man for our time because he is a man for all time!

The students applauded with apparent sincerity; Millicent Treadway applauded with apparent politeness. Hearthstone took a seat and Treadway rose to speak. She praised her colleague's presentation. Sort of. He was to be congratulated upon having made a case where there is none to be made. (She's being patronizing, thought Alice. Here, her linguistic sensitivity kicked in. Can a woman be "patronizing." She thought not. Matronizing? That word posed another problem. She put it on her mental shelf and went back to listening.) Treadway continued: "Permit me, Professor Hearthstone, to make a small correction in your summation. Matthew Arnold is not a man *for* all time. Rather he is a man *of* all time. He does

Can a woman be "patronizing." She thought not. Matronizing?

She called the class's attention to the "shining armor" of Sir Harold Hearthstone...

indeed bring together past and present, not in his vision but in his sexist traditionalism. You are correct, I believe, in taking the speaker of the poem to be Arnold and the auditor to be his wife. Consider, if you can, the tone of the poem in the context of that relationship. How patronizing! To address one's wife as a teacher might speak to a schoolgirl: 'There is a lesson to be learned, my dear.'" Treadway had fallen into her lower register in a creditable imitation of Hearthstone. "'Listen to your teacher now.' And what is to be learned?" The lower register yielded to a full upper register, almost a Wagnerian soprano. "That woman is to find her salvation in romantic love." She called the class's attention to the "shining armor" of Sir Harold Hearthstone and elicited some timorous giggles.

Treadway now read a parody entitled "Dover Bitch," and, although she had the text in hand, it was clear she knew the poem by heart and was practiced in its delivery. It was a feminist response to Arnold, and, in this context, a Treadway response to Hearthstone, who now rose in rebuttal, following applause for Treadway.
He recited again the relevant lines of "Dover Beach":

Ah, love, let us be true
To one another! for the world, which seems
To lie before us like a land of dreams,
So various, so beautiful, so new,
Hath really neither joy, nor love, nor light,
Nor certitude, nor peace, nor help for pain;

Hearthstone called attention, almost tremulously, to the mutuality of the call: "to one another." The speaker is himself vowing commitment.

In this regard, "he anticipates the Promise Keepers of our day." Here a few groans from the audience led the usually passionless Hearthstone to become uncharacteristically heated. "Mutual commitment! That is what marriage is about. And love: 'Ah, love, let us be true to one another.' To link love to entrapment is cynicism—feminism at its worst!"

Here, for the first time, one speaker interrupted the other, as Treadway boomed "Professor Hearthstone, I should like . . ."

"Silence!" cried Hearthstone. "I did not interrupt you."

"There are some things . . ."

"Silence!" There was a momentary silence. Then Hearthstone asked, "Professor Trigger, who has the floor?"

"Professor Hearthstone has the floor," responded Trigger, his face beaming with delight. "Carry on!" Alice sensed that Trigger was not encouraging civility. He was more like a referee breaking up a clinch. What had begun as an academic discussion was taking on the character of a sporting event. Treadway held her tongue, but began to tap rhythmically and audibly with her pencil as the Arnoldian continued.

Hearthstone's words now took on the hard edge of his indignation. He dismissed "Dover Bitch" as amateurish and unworthy of critique—"not so much a poem as a clumsy joke, its true nature readily evident to the 'remnant' but hidden from the Philistines."

Alice knew that Arnold's "remnant" were the bearers of culture from generation to generation, and Treadway must have known it too. Once more she interrupted.

"The Philistines," exclaimed Treadway, "were the enemies of the children of light." (She did know her Arnold.) "Ours is the

. . . Trigger . . . was more like a referee breaking up a clinch.

"You're not a Philistine, are you, love?"

new age of enlightenment. We are emerging from the darkness of the old conventional wisdom, which was conventional folly. It would have us believe that marriage is a mutual commitment, but in Arnold's day, as in millennia before, financial inequality was not a soil in which mutuality could flourish. And as for that word "love," it is among the most debased appellations in the English language. Dover Beach is in England, Harshtone (she began to deliberately mispronounce his name). In England, every sales clerk is called 'love': 'Could you wait on me, love?' 'Have you this in a larger size, love?' Actors call other actors 'love.'" Here Treadway turned to a female student in the first row. "Am I making sense, love?' The young woman nodded. To a young man: "You're not a Philistine, are you, love?" He returned a blank stare. She turned to Hearthstone: "Do you receive my meaning, love?"

A bell rang, signalling the end of the class period. Dr. Trigger rose to thank the speakers and ask for a final round of applause. He was beaming—elated with the success of the encounter. The usually composed Hearthstone was flushed and tight-lipped. A self-satisfied Treadway was immediately surrounded by female admirers.

Alice slipped out quietly and walked back to her room in meditation. Nineteenth-century England was her turf. Rather, to be exact, the impressions of that England in the mind of Lewis Carroll were her turf. She had her knowledge second hand, as it were, but she did feel she knew Matthew Arnold and understood his thought. She was present in the mind of Carroll as he read *Culture and Anarchy*. Arnold was in many ways a hopeless reactionary, resisting science in the schools and democracy in government. But he believed in civilized discourse, and he would have been appalled had he sampled a Jerry Trigger course. Today's session had its informative side, but in the end reminded Alice of a boxing match with Millicent Treadway landing a flurry of left jabs just before the bell.

Alice sighed and borrowed a little Latin from Carroll who had borrowed it from Cicero: "O, tempora! O, mores!" Then she raised her voice a little for only the trees to hear: "And for you Philistines, who need a translation: This is a fine mess you've gotten us into." Alice was not above borrowing from Oliver Hardy.

"This a fine mess you've gotten us into."

"MDs" In The Closet

"But I don't want to go among mad people," Alice remarked. *"Oh, you can't help that,* said the Cat, *"we're all mad here. I'm mad. You're mad."*
—The Annotated Alice, p. 89

A Politically Correct Alice?

...disorder and imprecision had been effectively exiled.

*T*hough Alice preferred the ground of Tradition for her excursions, both social and academic, she knew that safaris into the Postmodern world were necessary to her growth and academic advancement. The House of Blather was a house of delights, but it was not where the most significant or challenging questions were raised. Though it was fun to hear Blather speculate on what Keats might have written had he lived to the age of sixty, such speculation hardly moved forward the frontiers of knowledge. The Postmodern world was the cutting edge, no doubt about it. Whether it was cutting through to anything more valuable than what it had cut loose from was much in doubt, but that was where the action was.

It was on the Postmodern side of the wall that Alice, early on, had joined other new graduate students for a course entitled Research in English, taught by an au courant scholar named Lee Altmann. At first the course took Alice into the very antithesis of Wonderland. She became familiar with the *MLA International Bibliography*, the *MLA Directory of Periodicals*, and the *MLA Handbook*, and various computerized data banks. It was a world from which disorder and imprecision had been effectively exiled. Everything had a place; everything was in its place; anything new would be given a place. "Safer than the wall," thought Alice, and for a while she worked in complete security, following those procedures which guaranteed success.

...she must purge her language of all traces of patriarchy, sexism, racism, and other institutional evils.

But, alas, it is the nature of security to be short-lived. As Alice, travelling the road of the syllabus, passed from the vast but ordered universe of research through the confining but equally ordered chamber of documentation, she found herself entering a twisting passage called "Inclusive Language and Acceptable Terminology." Here Alice learned that, if she hoped to be published (or even do well in the course), she must purge her language of all traces of patriarchy, sexism, racism, and other institutionalized evils.

Some of the changes struck even this Victorian lass as reasonable and overdue, such as discontinuing the use of the masculine singular pronoun for common gender. Not that any of the alternatives were completely satisfactory. *He/she, him/her,* and *his/her* were all right for occasional use, but repetition of them undermined the rhythm and flow of discourse. Academic prose had little enough rhythm and flow in any case. *They, them,* and *their* as singulars would take some getting used to and would increase the indeterminacy of any text. Other changes seemed to Alice entirely satisfactory. The shift from *chairman* to *chairperson* to *chair* was welcome and effortless. But at what point did such language tampering move beyond the bounds of reasonable and tumble into the sort of wonderland best confined to fiction? Was a certain male student being serious or facetious in demanding that the offensive term *patriarchal* be banned from scholarly prose in favor of *fatherly*? And what about the white male who argued that the recently accepted *African-American* should be changed to *American-African* since *African* referred to a genetic and therefore more inherent reality while *American* indicated an accident of time and place? Whether this proposal was serious or not, it was as earnestly discussed as any other, except by Alice, who thought that the parade of substitutions had to end sometime. She had been familiar even in childhood with the difference between acceptable and non-acceptable terminology. A Victorian gentlewoman spoke of *limbs* rather than *legs*. But those standards were more long-lived: *limbs* had not replaced *legs* only to give way in a few years to *appendages* destined soon to give way to something else.

And how confusing it was to non-native speakers of English, who, like the other students, were required to rewrite assigned passages into academically acceptable English. No one, including Dr. Altmann, was able to explain to a Japanese student why she should not have changed "Amen, brother!" into "Aperson, sibling!"

Research in English was thus giving Alice her first exposure to "political correctness," though that expression was itself politically incorrect. Dr. Altmann taught "the diction of liberation" and demanded it of all his students. When someone joked about the matter, he was not amused. And so, when his teaching was satirized in a tongue-in-cheek student editorial, Altmann wrote an enraged response which only encouraged the campus wags to further frivolities. The anonymous editor had advanced many offbeat suggestions regarding the "diction of liberation" in a pseudo-scholarly, matter-of-fact tone. Changing *mailman* to *mailcarrier,* he(she?) argued, did not go far enough; the proper term would be *gendercarrier*. That suggestion was obviously too silly to be taken seriously by anyone. A recommendation that women be awarded Spinster of Arts degrees instead of Bachelor of Arts elicited rage from some quarters and amusement from others. But a paragraph on Alice drew support:

A recommendation that women be awarded Spinster of Arts degrees...

If all fictions are real, some might argue... that all realities are fictions.

A certain young woman among us has been maligned in being referred to as "fictional" —a term of disparagement if there ever was one. Alice is a victim of the hegemony of those who claim reality exclusively for their own state of being and refuse to recognize other forms of reality. The creations of the human mind realized in any form of art have had being bestowed on them, even as we have come into being from the mind of God. Alice is "differently real," and her reality should not be brushed aside by an insensitive use of language.

The point was cogently argued, and Alice found herself with many unwanted defenders. She had never objected to the label "fictional"; she had gloried in her fictional status; it was the secret of her immortality. If all fictions are real, some might argue (as would the March Hare, from whom Alice had first learned deconstruction criticism) that all realities are fictions. Some were already arguing that all history is fiction. "My fictionhood," she insisted "is my sisterhood with Hamlet and Portia; it's my *essence*."

"But here you are among us," argued Professor Van Lieder of the Philosophy Department, "and your existence must take precedence over your essence." Others in the Philosophy Department took issue with Lieder, and the whole controversy of essence vs. existence was given a new impetus. Alice was not happy with her new prominence, but Hugh was consoling: "The dispute is strictly academic, Alice. That's as unreal as anything ever gets."

Hugh's words were not the only consolation. There was a diversionary issue. The same editorial which challenged the labelling of Alice as "fictional" challenged the labelling of some students as "lazy." Such students are unfairly stigmatized by insensitive language; they are more properly seen as "motivationally disadvantaged." The editorial called for greater sensitivity to the motivationally disadvantaged in designing curricula, in giving out assignments, and in assigning grades. Students all over campus were snickering at so outrageous a suggestion, but support for the editor's argument was quick in coming. Lorenzo Ayuda, Distinguished Professor of Educational Psychology, affirmed in a guest column that "lazy" is not an accepted term in psychology, that motivational disadvantage is as genuine a psychological disorder as depression or paranoia, and that it is induced by a disparity between educational goals established by authorities and the felt needs of the afflicted students. Since the felt needs are real and the established goals arbitrary, it is the latter which must undergo alteration. Professor Ayuda called for a careful study to determine the felt needs of the motivationally disadvantaged and a subsequent redesigning of the curricula to meet those needs. Hank Barger, resident radical, provided further support, arguing that the punitive measures of failure, suspension, and expulsion taken against the motivationally disadvantaged constitute a civil rights violation.

There followed the most convincing proof one could possibly demand that the motivationally disadvantaged are not lazy: the formation of the Motivationally Disadvantaged Liberation Organization. Its members lobbied the Undergraduate Curriculum Committee. They filed "academic harassment" complaints with the Dean of Minority Affairs. They wrote letters to the student paper demanding that the University's antidiscrimination policy be

… "lazy" students are more properly seen as "motivationally disadvantaged."

...punitive measures of failure, suspension, and expulsion... constitute a civil rights violation.

amended to protect the motivationally disadvantaged. None of this fazed the administration until a retired attorney with a sense of humor and nothing to lose filed a class action suit against the University charging discrimination against the MD's, as they had come to be called. Without that lawsuit, the issue might have faded away; now, as a continuing controversy and the chief topic of humor, it spread outward from the campus to the city newspapers, the television news, and especially the radio talk shows. Callers-in told horror stories of how they had suffered at school and at home as members of a persecuted minority. They told of how they had rationalized that they were responsible for their own victimization. There were calls for MD support groups and federal funding of MD research. There was an ongoing and often impolite debate over the merits of the lawsuit.

The climax of this episode in the history of Parnassus University occurred, not in court, but in the spacious courtyard of a University dormitory. A stage had been erected at one end of the courtyard, and, had the dormitory been octagonal rather than rectangular, the resemblance to Shakespeare's Globe would have been striking. The groundlings crowded in, many wearing T-shirts proclaiming "NO PASSING ZONE" and "TALK BACK FOR THE RIGHT TO SLACK." The surrounding windows were filled with students and hung with banners proclaiming MD rights. There was live music, and the media were everywhere. Festivities began with the cheerleading squad warming up the crowd with "Fight! Fight! for MD rights!" after which there was a bombastic speech by the President of the MD Liberation Organization and an academic-style mini-lecture by Professor Ayuda on the nature and treatment of motivational disadvantage syndrome. All this was forgettable, but what followed was not. Luke Laffer took the stage—an aspiring comic, who was a cross between Jay Leno and Jesse Jackson. His theme was the failure of "closet MD's" to step forward and join the cause. Not too surprisingly, all of these closet MD's were faculty members, and Laffer led the crowd in an impassioned litany.

LAFFER: How many have found Professor Skipman during his posted office hours? [silence] Did anyone look in the closet? [laughter] Is he with us today? [cries of "no"] Professor Skipman,
CROWD: Come out of the closet!
LAFFER: How many take notes in Professor Oldman's course? [silence] You get the notes from your grandfather, don't you? [laughter] Is he with us today? [cries of "no"] Professor Oldman,
CROWD: Come out of the closet!
LAFFER: Professor Rambler set a record yesterday—twelve minutes on the course material. [shouts of disbelief] Is he with us today? [cries of "no"] Professor Rambler,
CROWD: Come out of the closet!

In all, nine faculty members were summoned, none of whom appeared. (That is, they did not appear at the rally. They later appeared in a student newspaper cartoon, above the caption "CLOSET STUFFING," which showed nine professors, some recognizable, trying to fit into a small closet, much as students used to stuff themselves into a telephone booth or a Volkswagen.) The crowd went home in high spirits, but after this one exuberant day, the movement went into

Not too surprisingly, all of these closet MD's were faculty members...

decline. A few days later the MD lawsuit was dismissed as "frivolous" by a judge who reprimanded the retired attorney but complimented the MDs on their extraordinary motivation. Soon university life was back to normal: Skipman was nowhere to be found during office hours; Oldman droned on from his age-ravaged notes; and Rambler rambled on. The motivationally disadvantaged had settled back into academic inertia. The god of laughter was taking a well-deserved vacation, and all was wrong with the world again.

When Research in English came to a close, Alice (fictional Alice!) had mastered every facet of the game. "It was a mad world there for a while, Alice," observed Hugh, looking back over the semester.

"Not mad, Hugh," corrected Alice, "just differently sane."

...a judge complimented the MD's on their extraordinary motivation.

Dr. Cory

"*So I wasn't dreaming after all,*"
she said to herself, "unless—unless
we're all part of the same dream.
Only I do hope it's my dream and
not the Red King's. I don't like
belonging to another person's dream,"...

–The Annotated Alice, p. 293

The Jung At Heart

There were times when the doctoral road reminded Alice of that Canterbury pilgrimage celebrated by Chaucer centuries ago, though Chaucer would not have understood the language of her academic contemporaries any more than most of them understood his.

"Whan that Chaucer of 'misprision' herde,"

Alice thought of that as the opening line for a Chaucerian view of English studies but knew she had no time for such a project. Here was another difference between the journey to Canterbury and her quest for a Ph.D. — little time for fellowship or for storytelling. Still, there was a great similarity in the richness of personality types. "God's plenty," Dryden had said of Chaucer's pilgrims. Alice thought she had at least as much material as Chaucer and a reasonable measure of literary talent. One day she would also have the time! It would be fun to play off Andrew Cory against Carla Viva. Cory was so hooked on archetypal theory that whatever course he taught became a pilgrimage to the shrine of Northrop Frye. Students generally referred to his course in non-fiction prose as "Bacon to Frye" and to Cory himself as "Little Sir Ego." Alice realized why when at a university colloquium he read an excerpt from his book *The Hero as*

"Students generally referred to his course in non-fiction prose as "Bacon to Frye..."

Hugh's eyes flashed approval...

Academician. It sounded conspicuously like a self-portrait. It also sounded incongruous, coming from this short, round-faced, freckled fellow with unruly hair, who looked like an aging Huck Finn. "At least he knows a hero when he is one," cracked Alice whose satirical eye was growing keener each quarter. Hugh's eyes flashed approval, but his lips said "careful." He was relieved that the humorless and ill-tempered Cory had not heard her. This pompous pedant, who emphasized color symbolism by using colored chalk, had flown into a rage one day when he found on his chalkboard "Heroes don't use colored chalk. — Trickster." His rage reached full fury when he was refused a thorough investigation by the noticeably snickering Chief of Security. Chaucer would have known what to do with Cory. Alice thought she knew too, and stored him away in her notebook.

Keeping Cory company in the same notebook was Carla Viva, a literary scholar of Jungian perspective who told and retold her more spectacular dreams everywhere — in class, in the faculty dining room, even on dates. Several suitors had been scared off, perhaps by her intensity, perhaps by her demand for psychic intimacy, perhaps because they felt they could never compete with her dreams as a source of excitement in her life.

She was the only professor from whose course Alice had withdrawn for fear of failure. The withdrawal was not without reason. Dr. Viva's students were expected to keep a dream log. It was not an absolute requirement ("invasion of privacy" warned the dean), but the alternative was a forty-page research paper to be graded by a presumably displeased professor. Few of the students dreamed as prolifically as Dr. Viva expected. She had especially high expectations of the veteran of Wonderland and the other side of the looking glass, but Alice fell miserably short of those expectations. Academic pursuits seemed to have dried up even her nocturnal imagination, and Lewis Carroll was no longer around to help. Other students had learned to play the game, concocting truly fascinating dreams over cheeseburgers or vegetarian pizza, most of them erotic fantasies, known to be Dr. Viva's preference. But Alice suffered from chronic high integrity, which, whether in the academic world or in the real world, can be as dangerous as high blood pressure. She could not fake her dreams and would have informed on her classmates had not Hugh counselled prudence.

"She must be told," Alice countered. "She has a book half-written, *Dreams of College Students: A Jungian Perspective.*"

"If you act on your integrity," cautioned Hugh, "you'll force her to act on hers. No one will thank you."

Alice agreed to play it safe. At least, she would be on the side of poetic justice. So she withdrew quietly from the course but not before recording the following incident in her notebook.

Dr. Viva had secured the student's permission for a class discussion of a most unusual dream. Wanda Sunset's dream-log entry read as follows on the class handout.

I found myself in a strange bedroom, decorated and furnished by someone of obvious taste and affluence. There were art objects from around the world—an African ceremonial mask on the wall, a set of primitive drums, even a totem pole in one corner. There were walnut bookcases filled with scholarly volumes, including many by Joseph Campbell and Mircea Eliade. Suddenly I became

...Alice suffered from chronic high integrity...

> *"I had never been there in reality. Had I been there in his dream?"*

aware that I was not alone, and turned to find Dr. Cory in his underwear smiling lustfully. I wanted to flee but was paralyzed with guilt. After all, I was an intruder. "I knew you would come," he told me. "They all do sooner or later." Then he was upon me, kissing me. "I must be dreaming," I thought out loud. "No," he replied, "I'm dreaming. You have entered my dream." Now he was fondling me and I was alarmed. "This isn't right," I protested. But he assured me, "You're not responsible for what happens in someone else's dream." At that point, he touched me very intimately and I woke up. The next morning, I spoke with Marie Schooler who house-sat for Dr. Cory during the summer and found that his bedroom was indeed furnished exactly as I had seen it. Where had my knowledge of Dr. Cory's bedroom come from? I had never been there in reality. Had I been there in his dream? That seems impossible, and yet . . .

Marie Schooler was an invited guest at the discussion, which could not have been livelier. Dr. Viva had heard tales of such dream-entries but had never met anyone with such an experience. She spoke of experiments in dream telepathy being conducted in the Dream Laboratory at Maimonides Hospital in Brooklyn. Dr. Viva favored a cautious approach, but thought the phenomenon quite compatible with the Jungian notion of a collective unconscious. No one could (or would) offer another explanation of Wanda's experience, and the professor found it hard to curb her excitement. When the discussion shifted to the symbolic significance of Cory's bedroom furnishings, which Dr. Viva "would love to see sometime," she made a potentially disastrous misstep. "Wanda, could you describe in more detail the African ceremonial mask and the Andean tapestry?"

"Andean tapestry, Dr. Viva?" The class searched the handout for the Andean tapestry. There was none.

"I thought you mentioned one." The professor seemed suddenly nervous.

"I didn't see a tapestry, Dr. Viva."

"My mistake. Tell us about the mask."

Wanda began rather haltingly to describe the mask. It was black. It had a nose . . . and mouth . . . and two eye openings. There were long pauses during which she tried to summon up additional details. It was during one of these pauses that a low, toneless, leaden voice was heard, like a voice from some other reality, penetrating their own. "It's above the bed." The voice was Marie Schooler's. Students and professor turned to stare at her. Another pause. "The Andean tapestry. It's above the bed."

There followed the kind of silence that shows you there is never perfect silence. The chirp of a cricket rang bright and clear. The forgotten hum of the expressway became loud and intrusive. The students gradually shifted their stares from Marie to Dr. Viva, who had shifted her stare to some unidentifiable point in space. "Someone say something," prayed Alice, and finally someone did. Lucy Adams shattered the silence, whether in mercy or in her naiveté Alice knew not. Cricket and expressway were submerged beneath the metallic clamor of Lucy's upper register. "Gosh, Dr. Viva, if you knew about the tapestry and you'd never been in the room, then you too must have entered one of Dr. Cory's dreams, even if you don't remember. That's exciting!"

It was the only explanation. Well, . . . the only respectable explanation. Everyone accepted it, and there followed a discussion

Dr. Viva thought the phenomenon quite compatible with the Jungian notion of a collective unconscious.

Chaucer would have known what to do with Hugh.

Alice wished that she did.

of questionable sincerity on the subject of Dr. Viva's possible out-of-body experience. The appropriate course of action (from a scholarly point of view) was obvious but long in being suggested. Finally Lucy said it: someone should ask Dr. Cory if he had ever in a dream "entertained" Wanda Sunset or Dr. Viva in his bedroom. "Who would like to do that?" asked an unenthusiastic Dr. Viva. It was a who-will-bell-the-cat question, and there were no takers. Dr. Viva never brought up the matter again, nor did anyone else, so that was the end of it. Well, . . .almost the end.

In December Alice accompanied Hugh Dumphrey to a cabaret-style party for faculty and graduate students, complete with band and soloists, provided by the music school. One of the evening's surprises was a song dedicated to Dr. Viva. The song was "Amore"; the singer came down to her table and crooned in a mellow baritone,

When you walk in a dream
But you know you're not dreaming,
Signora,
Scuza me but you see
Back in old Napoli
That's amore.

Dr. Viva looked pleased; Alice knew she wasn't. "Hugh, is this your doing?"

"Trickster." It was the only answer Alice got from him, but it told her more than she was asking. Chaucer would have known what to do with Hugh. Alice wished that she did.

Bella At Home

"It's a great huge game of chess that's being played —
all over the world — if this is the world at all, you know...

—The Annotated Alice, p. 208

An Acquisition And A Merger

$\mathcal{A}$lice had passed through the Vietnam War very much as Rip Van Winkle had passed through the American Revolution. Not that she had slept all that time. She is awake whenever children or the young at heart are turning the pages of *Alice in Wonderland* or *Through the Looking Glass* — probably every minute of every day. But, until she stepped off those pages and onto a university campus, it never occurred to real life people to tell her anything about the extra-literary world.

So she had entered the university knowing nothing of the Vietnam War or of the New University Conference, which had radically altered the proceedings of the Modern Language Association in the late 1960's. How fascinating it was when some senior faculty got off on that subject during an English Club gathering one December evening. The NUC, she learned, had been an organization of academic socialists who put radical politics at the heart of their university mission. The university was to be no longer an intellectual retreat amid a world of poverty, racism, sexism, and violence. The professor's primary mission was to enlist the student in the transformation of the world from capitalist exploitation to the justice that only socialism could effect. One impact of the NUC was to transform the MLA business meetings from sparsely attended, pro-forma gatherings into crowded, tension-charged battlefields on

The NUC...an organization of academic socialists who put radical politics at the heart of their university mission.

"*There was a time we could disagree politely.*"

which militant radicals assaulted the hastily constructed defenses of those committed to a largely unexamined traditionalism. Resolutions were introduced opposing the war, the literary canon, the patriarchal domination of the universities, etc., etc., etc. (Alice thought of the thunderings and bellowings from opposite sides of the wall and wondered if much had changed.) "Before those guys came along," observed Walter Thomas, the noted Victorian, "hardly anyone attended the business meeting—only those faithful souls who kept the organization going and a few curious newcomers. The NUC changed all that."

"More than that, old chap," interjected John Blather. "Civility went by the boards. There was a time we could disagree politely. If I liked Pope and my colleague preferred Goethe, we didn't insult each other; we exchanged ideas. That was cultural diversity at its best—no rancor, no forced feeding." Alice, who wondered about the limited scope of such diversity, was too polite to even disagree politely. Blather continued. "And the way those chaps presented themselves! Long stringy hair, dungarees—tramping through the hotel in workshoes with the laces flapping. 'Identifying with the working class,' they called it. Hmph! More like an insult to the working class!"

Feminist Edna Prober thought there was a positive residue from the NUC, especially in opening up the canon, and she even defended the incivility of those days with a story, familiar to all but Alice, about a mule and a two-by-four. Inevitably the name Hank Barger came up, and the senior faculty took as much delight in feeding Hank into Alice's imagination as Dickens must have taken in describing Miss

Havisham. Hank was a relic of the New University Conference, which with the end of the Vietnam War had vanished as quickly as it had appeared. Most of his fellows in the Conference had become assimilated (hateful word!) into an academe significantly transformed by their efforts. Academe had transformed them as well — mellowed them to a more civil tone, a diminished self-righteousness, even in some cases to a respect for the Blathers of their respective campuses. But Barger — never! Settle for modification when revolution had been the goal? His only concession (if it was such) was sneakers in place of the half-laced work shoes. There was still a job to be done, to be done, and a war to be won, to be won, and, if no one would lend a hand, he would go it alone. Alice, who admired ethical resolve wherever it might be found, felt a surge of unshared empathy for Hank Barger, whom she had not met.

She might never have met Hank, had it not been for a party given by Bella Montgomery, Dean of the Graduate School and a Boswell scholar. Bella too was an anachronism — more than that — she was out of place as well as out of time, and her home was as much an expression of her personality as John Blather's was of his. The pride of the old South held its ground in Yankee land: four massive brick pillars framing the double doors of an impressive Georgian brick. To pass through those double doors was to step into Tara: the lace curtains, the heavy drapes, the formal dining room, the portrait of Robert E. Lee, and the broad staircase which seemed incomplete without a descending Scarlett O'Hara. Completing the authenticity was Bella's live-in housekeeper, imported from Alabama. Though Bella was not so bigoted as to think that all professionals should

Bella too was an anachronism— more than that—she was out of place as well as out of time...

Verbal fireworks might well occur, but...

be white, she knew from tradition that domestic servants should be black, and, because she had not found a northern black as loyal and deferential as the position required, she had brought in Mattie Hawkins, polished her serving skills, and now spoke with pride of this necessary accessory to gracious hospitality.

What could have led Bella to invite into this island of the Old South the very antithesis of Southern graciousness, Hank Barger? (To cast her pearls before swine, her mother would have said.) Well, Bella had thought of Boswell's success in bringing together at a dinner party the Tory Samuel Johnson and his political opposite John Wilkes. To anyone but Boswell it would have appeared a prescription for disaster. But within a few short hours Johnson and Wilkes had earned each other's respect and even affection. Could Bella repeat Boswell's success? Not without trying. So she determined to bring together Hank Barger and Walter Huser, whose success as an entrepreneur had attracted the attention of President Reagan and drawn those two together into a mutual admiration society. Huser was also a trustee of the University, from whom the Development Office had great expectations, so there was financial risk in exposing him to Barger. But the added risk increased the appeal to Bella's Boswellian daring. Verbal fireworks might well occur, but had not Gerald Graff recommended bringing the conflicts of the world into an academic setting?

So the invitations went out. It was to be a small gathering, ensuring that Huser and Barger could not evade each other. One of the few invitations went to Alice (much sought after by party-givers) and another to Hugh, who had come to be regarded as her "significant other." (Hugh was not fond of the term and wondered if some people had "insignificant others.")

Alice and Hugh were overjoyed. A dinner at the home of Bella Montgomery! They had heard of the elegant mansion and of her charm as a hostess. "I wonder how many are invited and who they are," mused Alice. Hugh had no idea, no more than did Hank Barger or Walter Huser.

So Alice and Hugh set out for the Montgomery mansion on the appointed day, with no anticipation of conflict, only of charm, of elegance, and of that famous Southern cuisine. They were greeted at the door by Bella Montgomery herself, voluptuous as well as charming, swelling above a low-cut gown, contoured to her full figure. "Ah'm so pleased y'all could come," she drawled in an accent Hugh categorized as 'self-consciously authentic.' They were escorted into the living room, where appetizers abounded and Mattie took their drink orders. Others arrived, all nicely dressed; introductions were made; and conversation was natural in so stimulating an environment. Walter Huser was the most confident man that either Alice or Hugh had ever met. He seemed able to speak with authority on an astounding range of subjects and seemed completely at ease with everyone. It didn't take Hugh long to realize that Huser's apparent omniscience was created by his skillful control of conversation. A dispute over the awarding of a Pulitzer Prize became speculation over its effect on sales. A discussion of football quickly focussed on the profitability of franchises. "He wouldn't know a slot-formation from a shotgun," whispered Hugh, "but he's as shifty as any running back." Alice didn't know a running back from a goal post, but Hugh's point was not lost on her.

Hugh was not fond of the term and wondered if some people had "insignificant others."

"A whukman's tonic, Mistah Huser? Ah ain't nevah heerd a sech a thing."

Hank Barger arrived late and without apology, and was immediately introduced to Alice. He assured her—rather loudly, she thought—that he did not hold her, a fictional character, responsible for the sufferings of the human race. The remark seemed intended more for the ears of others than her own, and Walter Huser immediately made his way across the room. He greeted Hank affably and there followed an exchange for which a score-card might have been appropriate. Walter told of his support of the soup kitchens; Hank challenged the economic system that made them inevitable. Walter mentioned the upcoming charity ball; Hank asked what Mrs. Huser's gown would cost. Hank was up 30-love when Walter rallied. Hank spoke of the unemployment rate, Walter of plans to increase his work force; Hank spoke of the need for housing, Walter of how that need had led him to move into the construction business. Alice listened fascinated. "Overcoming him with yesses," whispered Hugh, who had read *Invisible Man*. Indeed, that seemed to be the game Walter was playing, but he went too far, thought Alice, when Hank spoke of "not setting ourselves above the working class." Mattie was making a last round with the appetizer tray when Walter formally introduced her to Hugh and offered to pass the tray while the two of them got acquainted. Mattie, of course, declined and would have gone about her errand had not Walter ordered a "workman's tonic."

"A whukman's tonic, Mistah Huser? Ah ain't nevah heerd a sech a thing." (Bella was especially pleased with Mattie's Butterfly McQueen accent.)

"I can make my own, Mattie. Just show me where to find the ingredients." And the two went off to the kitchen where they remained for a long time. "Suspiciously long," thought Alice. When Walter reappeared, his face had been strikingly transformed. "The Cheshire Cat," gasped Alice. Hugh soberly nodded agreement; he feared a deadly storm.

Soon they were summoned to dinner, which lived up to expectations. Bella was proud of her linens, her china, her silver, her gumbo, her praline dessert, and, of course, her Mattie, whose service was impeccable. But Bella's supreme triumph was the interchanges between Hank and Walter, who was going out of his way to be agreeable, congratulating Hank on his new book, asking about his children, suggesting they have lunch sometime, . . . Here was that reconciliation of opposites which Coleridge had identified as a principle of unity. "How well Walter and Hank are getting along," whispered Bella. Alice agreed. "Too well," thought Hugh, but he nodded politely.

Bella was basking in Boswellian self-congratulation when trouble came from the least expected source. "Dean Montgomery, ah sho' could use some hep wi' the pots n pans, n since Professah Bahger ain' dressed up, mebbe he wouldn' mine hep'n." Mattie looked expectantly at Hank Barger; the other guests looked expectantly at Hank Barger; Hank Barger looked expectantly at Bella, who looked mortified. "Ah jes thought that since Mistah Bahger come in his wuk clothes, . . ." Mattie was cut off by a gasp from Bella.

The one island of composure in that sea of consternation was Walter Huser, who had risen before anyone realized it, was removing his jacket, and was volunteering his services in the kitchen. "Bella, allow me. I washed many a cooking pot before I struck it rich, and

When Walter reappeared, his face had been strikingly transformed.

(That's the trouble with being a fictional character. Your whole history is already known to the world.)

to tell the truth, I've missed it." By this time he had his arm around Mattie. "Comrade, let's get to it!"

Hank suspected he had been set up, but could not clearly assess his options. Should he belatedly offer his services in the kitchen? An offense to the hostess. Should he commiserate with Bella? A betrayal of the working class. Should he rise up in anger? At whom? Certainly not at Bella. At Mattie? At Huser, probably, but. . .

The guests shared Bella's embarrassment in near silence for a few very long moments. Alice thought of diverting them with wonders from the other side of the Looking Glass, but realized that they already knew them. (That's the trouble with being a fictional character. Your whole history is already known to the world.) After some fumbling attempts at conversation on the part of all, Hugh thanked the hostess for "a truly wonderful evening" and said that he and Alice really must be going. The others followed their example, Bella saw them to their cars, good-byes were exchanged with forced gaiety, and the guests departed.

As she turned back to the house, Walter Huser emerged, and Bella apologized profusely for how badly the evening had turned out. "Nonsense, Bella, it turned out wonderfully. I've never enjoyed myself more!" He seemed to mean it. He too departed, and Bella was free to confront Mattie, whom she found in the kitchen, humming a spiritual and smiling contentedly. "Ah s'pose you know you're fired, Mattie."

"Yes, Miss Montgomery, ah know." The Butterfly McQueen dialect had disappeared as abruptly as the New University Conference. Mattie's speech was hardly distinguishable from Bella's.

"You'll be treated better than you deserve. I'll give you a week's severance and pay your way back to Alabama."

"Ah'm not going back to Alabama. Monday, ah starts to work for Mr. Huser. Ah'll have mah own apartment and double what ah's been earning heah. Kin move in tonight if ah wants."

Mattie did move that night, and the absence of Scarlett O'Hara on the staircase was not the only void in that outpost of the old South.

The story could end here, but lest readers conclude that Bella's efforts had failed, that there had been no Boswellian success, no Coleridgean reconciliation of opposites, this tale requires a coda.

Early the next day Bella phoned Hank Barger with a profuse apology, and the most well born of Southern gentry could not have responded with more graciousness than Hank. It was the beginning of a new friendship, by which the world population of significant others was increased by two. Bella's charm and no small part of her wealth came to be utilized in causes espoused by Hank Barger. And Hank? From that day forward, he grew in graciousness in the eyes of all. There are still parties at the Montgomery mansion — classless affairs at which Bella and Hank, as co-hosts, serve the monied and the destitute, the well-born and the low-born, academic luminaries and academic strugglers. Every Saturday, the Coalition for the Homeless has a working luncheon at the Montgomery mansion. Y'all come! Y'heah?

...the world of significant others was increased by two.

"*If there's no meaning in it,*" *said the King,* "*that saves a world of trouble,
you know, as we needn't try to find any.
And yet, I don't know,*" *he went on, spreading the verses on his knee,
and looking at them with one eye;
*"*I seem to see some meaning in them after all . . .*"

—The Annotated Alice, p. 159

A Night of Poetic Disenchantment

Alice was elated. She had been appointed graduate student representative on the Visiting Poets Committee. From childhood, she had been a lover of verse, mostly that of the nineteenth century. As a graduate student, she had expanded her knowledge of poetry and had come to love the older poets, especially Milton and Donne. But it was her response to twentieth-century poets that had been most valued by her professors. And no wonder. Until now, the chief indicator of literary greatness had always been the judgment of future generations. Shakespeare had endured; Milton had endured; Blake and Melville had not only endured but risen dramatically in reputation. Future generations had a certain credibility because of cultural distancing. But with the reappearance of Alice in the late twentieth century, it had become possible for a literary work to be evaluated by the cultural distancing of the past. How does at least one Victorian (fictional though she be) respond to the work of T. S. Eliot? of Auden? of Adrienne Rich? Never before had such questions been answerable. Not that everyone valued her opinions. Her enthusiasm for T. S. Eliot was a confirmation of greatness among those who shared that enthusiasm; it was dismissed contemptuously by those who consider Eliot irrelevant and superseded. "It's no reflection on you one way or the other, Alice," observed Hugh. "It's a question of whose saint is being haloed."

In spite of the controversies over her judgments, her unique

Until now, the chief indicator of literary greatness had always been the judgment of future generations.

"...since members of the committee are unfamiliar with who's who...I take responsibility."

perspective made Alice an obvious choice for the Visiting Poets Committee, selected and chaired by the current Poet-in-Residence, Red Archer. Archer was a visual stereotype (by intent?) of a contemporary poet: medium long hair bound by a rubber band in back, gym shoes, blue jeans, black turtleneck, and a single earring. Alice arrived for the first committee meeting with a short list of nominees for the poetry series. Archer thanked her for her suggestions, assuring her that he would keep her list "on file for future reference." He, in turn, presented the Committee with a list of the five poets who would be visiting during the coming year and asked for a motion that the list be accepted. The motion was made and seconded before Alice could absorb what was happening. "Any discussion?"

"Yes," replied Alice. "Well, not a discussion exactly, but could I have a clarification? I thought that it was the Committee's job to draw up the list of visiting poets."

"The slate of visiting poets is a Committee decision. That is the thrust of the motion before us." Archer was patient and indulgent with this novice in the world of committee work. "But, since members of the Committee are unfamiliar with who's who in contemporary poetry, I take responsibility for making the selections."

"Then why have a committee?" asked Alice, surprised at her boldness.

"More democratic. Besides," Archer added, "there will be other work for the Committee: publicizing the readings, organizing receptions, . . .You'll be very involved."

"I see." What Alice saw was that he needed an office assistant, not a committee, if he needed anybody at all! But she was not quite bold enough to say that, so she gave her "aye" in a unanimous vote to invite five poets whom she had never heard of.

Archer proceeded to take care of some routine matters, mostly assigning responsibilities for the mundane details of the first reading in the series, then asked, "Is there any new business?"

Alice had no new business, but she took advantage of the opening. Was there a policy being followed in setting up the Visiting Poets Series? "For example, is it assumed that each poet will read his or her own poems?"

"Of course," replied Archer. "Of course," replied the raised eyebrows of other Committee members.

Alice felt a bit foolish but pursued her point. "It's just that the few poets I've heard don't read poetry very well — not even their own. Wouldn't it be better to have someone with dramatic talent — perhaps someone from the Department of Theater Arts — read the poems? The poet could still introduce them and comment on them."

"Any discussion?" There was a reluctance in Archer's voice that led Alice to suspect that he had been personally offended. A young assistant professor dismissed her suggestion as "a Victorian notion," and Alice felt what Mary Lynn Johnson had called "the arrogance of the present toward the past." "I'm a victim of time prejudice," thought Alice, wondering if it was really different from racial prejudice or religious prejudice or any other prejudice. But she kept these thoughts to herself and argued a practical point rather than a principle. "Perhaps the poor delivery of the poets has something to do with the low turnout at poetry readings. If the work of a widely admired poet were well presented. . ."

"The low turnout is due to the backwardness of the University

So she gave her "aye" in a unanimous vote to invite five poets whom she had never heard of.

"Our poetry readings will never be popular, Alice."

community. It is due in part to the narrowminded traditionalism of our senior faculty." It was not Archer who had responded, but Arthur Sayler, a young postmodernist who, at the age of thirty-five, had three books to his credit. Sayler would have gone on, had not Archer intervened.

"Our poetry readings will never be popular, Alice. It's not our mission to entertain but to expand horizons. We could increase attendance by bringing in established poets; we don't. We invite those who are ringing in the changes, discarding old forms, breaking new ground. I've glanced at your suggestions for our series: Richard Wilbur, Denise Levertov, David Ignatow — it tells me that you are hooked on the star system. I grant that a Wilbur reading would be well attended; I grant also that the audience would hear a skilled performer. But would they leave the reading changed? thinking not just new *things* but in new *ways*?"

Alice settled into silence. She thought but did not say: I would be satisfied, at last occasionally, to hear some of my favorite poetry beautifully rendered. She wondered but did not ask: who decided the mission of the Visiting Poets Series? Archer? Last year's Committee? She awakened from her meditation in time to hear the term "language poetry." The first poet in the series, Ralph Dare, was a "language poet." Sayler voiced his approval. Other Committee members showed interest. Alice sat on in silence, wondering what any poetry was if it were not language. It occurred to her that "poetry" is sometimes used analogously, that ballet and even ice dancing are occasionally described as "poetry in motion." However, the language poets were distinguishing themselves not from ballet dancers but from other poets. From nonlanguage poets, presumably. Alice left the meeting with her curiosity aroused but her enthusiasm diminished.

Hugh was no help. He knew nothing of "language poets." So Alice, who had her course work to be concerned about, awaited demystification from the mouth of Ralph Dare himself.

When the big evening of the small audience arrived, Alice was there, notebook in hand, escorted by Hugh, and was introduced to Ralph Dare by Red Archer. He thanked her for coming, he was glad to meet her, he had heard about her, he hoped she would find his presentation interesting, etc., etc. Alice then joined the other seven members of the audience, and Red Archer introduced the visiting poet. From the introduction, Alice learned that, though language poetry is not an organized or homogeneous movement, this diverse group have certain things in common. First of all, they "objectify language" — the words and phrases are not conveyors of something but the something itself. Secondly, a language poet does not express meaning but opens up the possibility of meaning — he [Archer was patriarchal in his language] sets in motion a process through which the reader engages with the poet in a quest for meaning. Thirdly, language poets do not attempt to construct ordered discourse. Language poetry is characterized by discontinuity. It shocks the reader out of his conditioned expectations and into an openness to unlimited possibilities. Archer moved on to the subject of the "up-and-coming" Ralph Dare's yet-to-be-recognized greatness and his uniqueness. "Ralph Dare is a *collage* poet," proclaimed Archer. "I'll let him tell you what that is."

Ralph Dare looked a bit old to be "up-and-coming." Alice studied the lined face, the shock of snow-white hair, the slow shuffle

"Ralph Dare is a collage poet," proclaimed Archer. "I'll let him tell you what that is."

But coherence is an instrument of artistic tyranny…

to the lectern. "At least sixty, probably sixty-five," thought Alice. "A twentieth-century Father William?" But, in spite of the unmistakable signs of age, he was youthful in his enthusiasm.

"Collage poetry is a very simple thing," Dare assured his small audience. "You've all seen visual collages — art works of the cut-and-paste variety? The collage poet juxtaposes not visuals but phrases, with this additional difference: the visual artist generally aims at some thematic coherence. He [Dare was likewise patriarchal in his language] might put together images of Hitler, Mussolini, goose-stepping soldiers, war planes, dead bodies, and the like, so that the viewer says 'Fascism' or 'man's inhumanity to man.' The coherence of the collage steers the viewer's response. But coherence is an instrument of artistic tyranny: an indirect means of thought control. Collage poetry by shunning coherence stimulates the mind to respond freely to the poem. Listen now to one of my earlier efforts." He read with the flattest delivery that Alice had ever heard:

tell me where is fancy bred
wake Duncan with thy knocking
jest and youthful jollity
Lady Teazle, Lady Teazle, I'll not bear it.
I wear the chains I forged in life
rise and shine! rise and shine!
we are such stuff as dreams are made of
nor yet the last to lay the old aside
make me a willow cabin at thy gate

"Did you notice my lack of inflection?" He beamed at his audience. "Deliberate! To read the poem dramatically might prejudice the audience response, which must be absolutely free." At this point Dare distributed copies of his poem and asked to hear responses. One of the bolder members of the audience, a clean-cut, conservative-looking undergraduate, blurted out: "There's nothing to respond to. The poem makes no sense. Not one of the nine lines has anything to do with the other eight."

"Ah, there you are wrong, my friend. Any two things have possibilities of relationship — infinite possibilities. Remember what T. S. Eliot said in 'The Metaphysical Poets'?

> . . .the ordinary man's experience is chaotic, irregular, fragmentary. The latter falls in love, or reads Spinoza, and these two experiences have nothing to do with each other, or with the noise of the typewriter or the smell of cooking; in the mind of the poet these experiences are always forming new wholes.

Eliot was right about the need for connections but wrong in assigning that responsibility to the poet. Language poetry — especially collage poetry — assigns it to the reader, calls upon Eliot's ordinary man to be extraordinary." Dare held up his poem and tapped the text dramatically. "It is the indeterminacy of relationships that makes language poetry a catalyst of meaning."

A young woman in pseudo-gypsy attire attacked from another angle: "What's so great about this poem? Anyone can string together nine random lines of poetry."

"Precisely!" Dare beamed more brightly. "And that's the answer to those who criticize language poets for being elitist. Collage poetry is not only accessible to everyone — it can be created by everyone, even by non-readers, as I'm going to show you now. The lines of collage

"There's nothing to respond to. The poem makes no sense."

"If no connection emerges... the failure is in our imaginations."

poetry need not be taken from the realm of literature as that term is narrowly understood. They can come from stock market reports, baseball broadcasts, anywhere at all! So let's create a poem, shall we?" With that, Dare handed each member of the audience a slip of paper on which to write a phrase or short sentence which would become a line in a collage poem. Dare then collected the entries and wrote them randomly on the chalk board. Alice saw the following poem take form — no, accumulate — before her very eyes.

The Dow rose seventeen points to close at 8412.
The cow jumped over the moon.
no left turn
Here's Johnny!
Read my lips: no new taxes.
latitude 32°, longitude 11°
The New York Times Book Review
I'm not a crook.

Dare beamed brighter than ever. "Now we interact with the poem to generate meaning. If no connection emerges between the second line and the first, the failure is in our imaginations. No possible interpretation must be dismissed." For a few moments, Dare's gaze of expectancy faced off against eight expressions of puzzlement.

Then a young woman spoke up, not the pseudo-gypsy but someone well tailored and reflective. "I see a gender connection. A rising market is a bull market — a sexist term implying that the world of high finance is a male world. The second line prophesies the ascendancy of woman in that world."

Dare responded with a smile and a nod of approval. Then a young man in a Coors T-shirt that stopped a few inches short of his size-46 dungarees responded with a smirk. "I agree that 'cow' is a good metaphor for 'woman,' but I think 'jumped over the moon' means that she missed her period." This respondent was angrily set upon by several women, but he appealed to the poet for support: "No possible interpretation must be dismissed. Right, Mr. Dare?" The poet appealed for civility but without success; several women were in the mood for a low-tech lynching. So Red Archer brought the session to a premature close. He thanked Ralph Dare for a "memorable" presentation. "The richness of collage poetry is in the dynamic and diverse response that it excites in its audience. We have all experienced that here tonight. Ralph, we thank you for enriching us this evening." Archer led the audience in polite, short-lived applause. Dare was clearly pleased with himself.

Hugh and Alice slipped out the door while three women set upon the slouching Coors endorsement. "Well, Hugh, what connections did you make?"

Hugh reflected a few moments. "I connect Dare's collage poetry with Harold Bloom's 'anxiety of influence.' Dare is a split personality rebelling against multiple poet-father figures in an Oedipal orgy. I see language poetry as a psychological class action suit against the established poets."

"Not bad, Hugh. Write that up for one of the journals."

"And what connections did you make, Alice?"

"All I could think of was that song in *Gypsy*, 'You Gotta Have a Gimmick,' sung by three strippers."

"Maybe poetry is a striptease of the soul."

"Another journal article there, Hugh. You're on a roll."

The poet appealed for civility but without success; several women were in the mood for a low-tech lynching.

The Nightmare Exam

"Alice thought the whole thing very absurd,
but they all looked so grave that she did not dare to laugh; ..."

—The Annotated Alice, p. 50

A Circle In The Square

"Why?" A question not to be asked...

It was a transformed Alice who stood on the verge of doctoral status. Where was the insecure, deferential young woman who had shared the security of the wall with Hugh Dumphrey a few years ago? In her place was a self-confident scholar who had come to enjoy those "safaris" to the left of the wall, cutting through the postmodern tangle with what Hugh Dumphrey called her "machete of the mind." This new Alice had occasionally shocked fellow students by her willingness to question requirements and even enter into disputes with her mentors on the graduate faculty.

The first dispute she had lost. She would have to acquire a reading knowledge of French and German. "Why?" A question not to be asked, but, having been asked, requiring an answer. "To be able to do scholarly research in those languages," replied her advisor.

"In what languages do you do scholarly research?" Alice was surprised at her boldness.

"Only in English."

"But don't you. . ."

"I didn't say you must *do* research in two other languages, only that you must be *able* to." A distinction worthy of Wonderland. It was a battle she had lost, and she acquired her minimal, transient competence in German and French as required.

But the other major battle she had won. Alice was under

...entrance into the mind of an author is never possible.

extreme pressure to do a dissertation which would break new ground in literary theory or at least apply contemporary theory in some impressive way. But she had long ago decided on a very different topic, and she held her ground: *Inside the Mind of Lewis Carroll.* So radical was her proposal that she was called before the graduate English faculty to defend it. Professor Stan Lee Shark, noted for his work in reader-response theory, argued that the reader's response is always an act of creation, that entrance into the mind of an author is *never* possible. "We can't get into the mind of Lewis Carroll, Alice." Other faculty agreed with Shark.

Alice's face wore a smile of victory even as she replied, "*You can't get into the mind of Lewis Carroll, but I have been there.*" Alice got her way and generated the most unique dissertation ever. (Yes— some things are more unique than others.)

Only one hurdle remained for Alice, the "formality" of her oral examination. It was a foregone conclusion that she would pass, having written with authority on a world about which her examiners could only make inferences. But none of us are so knowing that we do not have moments of doubt, nor so confident that we are immune from anxiety. The night before her orals, Alice sat at her desk, her dissertation before her, trying to imagine what questions might be asked. The futility soon exhausted her, her head began to nod, and the words ran together into darkness.

When the darkness had slid backward into dusk, her desk had turned into a long picnic table, and she was seated in the middle of a wooden bench. There were trees silhouetted against a dusky sky. "I'm out of doors," she thought, "in a place I've never been before." There were round orange paper lanterns strung from pole to pole within some sort of enclosure, and Alice recognized the face grinning from each lantern. "The Cheshire Cat!" Then she heard a disturbingly familiar voice, harsh and reprimanding: "We've been waiting for you!" "The Queen of Hearts," exclaimed Alice, and there gradually took shape three figures directly across the table from her. In the middle sat the Queen, clearly recognizable in her voice and royal robes but with the facial features of the feminist scholar Edna Prober.

"Well, she *did* come, my dear." This mellow voice emanated from the King of Hearts at the Queen's right, but his kindly features were those of the Victorian specialist, Walter Thomas.

"If we don't begin, we'll never get started." Alice at once recognized this cantankerous speaker to the left of the Queen by appearance and demeanor to be the March Hare but with the countenance of Professor Stan Lee Shark.

"Yes. Let's do. We can never award a prize if we don't begin," came an eager reply from Alice's left.

"Why, Dodo. How good of you to come. Oh, dear!" Alice had just seen a striking resemblance between the Dodo's features and those of Professor Oldman, but, since the birdman simply nodded mindlessly, an apology seemed unnecessary.

"We all know each other, so I see no need for introductions." The Queen was aggressively formal. "Let the examination begin!"

Alice was not sure she *did* know these creatures. Were they from her past or from her present? And which Alice was she? The twentieth-century woman or the nineteenth-century girl? She experienced a familiar shrinking feeling and her self-confidence

And which Alice was she?

"She's in the mind of Lewis Carroll and doesn't know where she is."

seemed to be shrinking as well. "All four of you seem doubly familiar, but. . ."

"Four? Four?" interjected the March Hare in a frenzy. "She can't count!"

"She can't count!" echoed the Queen. "Write that down." And the King, as though he were a secretary, dutifully did so.

"Perhaps she didn't notice the gentleman to her right," suggested the King when he had finished his notation. It was true. Alice had completely overlooked the Dormouse/Professor Rambler figure dozing against the table.

A sharp rap of the Queen's scepter near his nose roused him abruptly. "Say hello to Alice."

"Hello to Alice." The Dormouse blinked his eyes, took a drink from the tankard before him, and his head fell back on the table with a small thud.

At this point, Alice became aware that there were a number of tankards on the table. "Where are we? You all look familiar, but this place is very strange."

"She's in the mind of Lewis Carroll and doesn't know where she is," snorted a contemptuous March Hare.

"Oh, my!" exclaimed a disappointed Dodo.

"It's the seventh square, Alice dear." The King was kind and patient as always. "If you reach the eighth, you'll be hooded."

"The seventh square?" questioned Alice. "This doesn't look at all like the forest where I met the White Knight over a century ago."

The March Hare's tone was one of rebuke: "Things do change, child! It's now the Fear Garden, and we are the Fear Merchants.

You haven't touched your tankard, have you? — out of touch with your surroundings obviously."

"Drink, girl!" commanded the Queen. "Off with its head!" Alice drank from the foam-topped tankard and felt herself tremble and shrink a bit more. "First question, Dodo." The Queen's tone made it sound like a death sentence.

Dodo seemed as intimidated by the Queen as was Alice. He reluctantly asked, "What kind of frog is the Frog-Footman in *Alice in Wonderland?*"

Alice tried to think of varieties of frogs, but all that ran through her mind, so repeatedly that no other thought could make an entry was "A frog is a frog is a frog." When she finally spoke, it was only to break the unbearable silence. "An ordinary frog, may it please Your Majesty."

"It does not please My Majesty! An answer more worthy of a frog-gigger than of a scholar. Species, please!"

There was another moment of silence. "She doesn't know," interjected the Dodo disappointedly.

"She doesn't know!" The March Hare's tone was unfriendly.

"She doesn't know," the Queen pronounced with finality. "Write that down!" And she banged her scepter upon the table near the nose of the startled Dormouse. "The answer is leap-frog!"

"And very good leap-frog milk it is," muttered the Dormouse. He took a swig from the tankard and again slumped into slumber.

"But leap-frog isn't a frog," pleaded Alice. "It's a game."

"All frogs are game to a frog-gigger." The Queen's tone was commanding: "Next question, March Hare."

"Tell us, if you can, how many oysters the Walrus ate." The

When she finally spoke, it was only to break the unbearable silence.

"Off with her head!"

March Hare was in his own way as confrontational as the Queen and almost as intimidating.

"I don't know."

"She doesn't know," mocked the March Hare.

"She doesn't know," echoed the Queen.

"No one kept count," protested Alice, "not even the Walrus."

"Lewis Carroll was a mathematician," countered the March Hare. "He would have kept track of the number."

"The number isn't important." Alice was becoming more irritated than intimidated.

"Mathematics doesn't count—make a note of that," directed the Queen.

The King in his role as secretary pronounced the words slowly as he recorded them: "There's no accounting for mathematics."

"But I didn't say that!" protested Alice.

"You said something very like it," replied the Queen.

"Like it or not, it didn't mean the same thing." Alice was becoming defiant.

"Meaning is created in the listener response," lectured the March Hare.

"You're incompetent—all of you!" shouted Alice. She felt herself inexplicably growing larger.

"Off with her head!" shrieked the Queen, and she swung at Alice with her scepter. Ducking, Alice struck her head hard upon the picnic table. When she opened her eyes, she was alone in her room, the picnic table had reverted to a desk, dawn was breaking, and she could feel a hickey rising on her forehead.

"It was only a dream," thought Alice. "A dreamer should know she's dreaming, but she never does."

It was an apprehensive Alice who appeared before her dissertation committee that morning. As it turned out, there was nothing to be feared. Professor Prober could not have been nicer. Stan Lee Shark was friendlier than she had ever seen him, and he offered her a rare invitation: would Alice like to collaborate with him on a study of the correlation between authorial intent and reader response. He offered her this opportunity as though he were offering an unrefusable gift. Here Alice made her first slip-up in an up-to-now perfect performance. She turned to Professor Oldman at her left and asked: "Do you think I should, Dodo?" Oldman smiled mindlessly and said nothing. There was an embarrassed silence which was soon broken by a loud snore from her right: Rambler had fallen into a deep sleep. All the tension which Alice had concealed so effectively became channelled into uncontrollable laughter.

"Alice, you're losing your head," said Professor Prober in the mildest of reprimands.

"It *is* quite funny, my dear," gently interposed Walter Thomas. "Rambler dozing off like that."

"You must control those laughing fits, Alice," admonished Shark. "You don't want your students to think you're hare-brained."

To the puzzlement of the committee, Alice's laughter intensified, and it became doubtful whether the examination could proceed. Professor Prober declared a recess and suggested Alice take a walk, which she did until she had recovered from her fit of humor.

In the end, she passed her examination with ease and promised

"Alice, you're losing your head."

The white knights of academe ride library chairs and office chairs and sometimes distinguished professor chairs...

to tell her examiners "one day" what could possibly have been so funny. Her mind went back to her childhood episode on the seventh square, listening to the White Knight explain his preposterous inventions and watching him repeatedly fall from his horse. Was he fictional or differently real? The white knights of academe ride library chairs and office chairs and sometimes distinguished professor chairs, and they almost never fall off, secured as they are by their tenure belts. But are their inventions less preposterous than those of the fictional White Knight? A question worth exploring one day.

Meanwhile, she was free to claim her prize. She moved to the eighth square and accepted the queenly hood of the doctorate. Walter Thomas was pleased; John Blather made a bad joke about Queen Victoria doctored up; Hugh Dumphrey was beaming with pride; and Dodo/Oldman was in his glory: a prize had been given, and he adjusted to perfection Alice's tassel and hood.

The Phallocentrism
Lecture

*Lastly, she pictured to
herself how this same
little sister of hers
would, in the aftertime,
be herself a grown
woman; and how she
would keep, through
all her riper years, the
simple and loving heart
of her childhood; . . .*

—The Annotated Alice, p. 164

Alice In Ecstasy

Congenial companion- ship is the great deconstructor of misery...

For years Hugh Dumphrey and Alice had traveled their rocky road, tradition on the right, postmodernism on the left. It was like living continually amid those frontal disturbances pointed out on weather maps. "Blow, winds, and crack your cheeks! rage! blow!" had become their favorite line, spoken always with a mock seriousness which Shakespeare would have approved under the circumstances.

At the end of those four years, the weather-beaten pair had secured tenure and doctorate respectively, to go with a healthy toleration of frontal disturbances. Their new status was adequate compensation for the ordeal, which had not been such an ordeal after all. Congenial companionship is the great deconstructor of misery, and this pair had proven extraordinarily compatible so much so that Hugh thought their compatibility could surely endure the trials of marriage. Alice, who had become a more scientific humanist than Hugh, was cautious. "Let's check it out," she said, and proceeded to do so.

Seated before the latest IBM hardware with the Compatibility IV software, she began putting in the relevant data for each potential spouse: curriculum vitae, psychological profile, horoscope — even their embarrassingly low sexual I.Q.'s. When she pushed the answer key, there immediately appeared on the screen two columns, entitled respectively, "On the one hand/On the other hand." With visible

It bothered Hugh that a machine rather than Alice had responded to his proposal...

annoyance, Alice interrupted the program and typed in "This is not an academic question!" After some fiddling, she called up a triple option on the screen:

Choose one:

I) information mode

D) decision mode

S) storage mode

She struck the D key and the monitor flashed

GO FOR IT!

It bothered Hugh a bit that a machine rather than Alice had responded to his proposal, but he had adjusted enough to the postmodern world to accept it. Should he kiss Alice or the computer? He kissed Alice, who returned his kiss with IBM-quality assurance. IBM lets you do great things.

And so Alice and Hugh planned a wedding in the University Chapel, where they had so often found repose during their four-year trek along that stony elevated path. Alice asked Professor Walter Thomas to escort her down the aisle. He was an eminent Victorian scholar, who knew her better than any living person. He knew also that she had really wanted the obviously unavailable Lewis Carroll. Fortunately, Professor Thomas had an imagination and a flair for the dramatic unusual among Victorian scholars. He conspired with the Theatre Arts Department to surprise Alice, and, when the bride arrived at the Chapel in off-white Victorian lace, she was met by the most reasonable facsimile of Lewis Carroll one could ever expect to encounter.

It was a wedding not only memorable but memorialized, the

only wedding ever to be written up in *Victorian Studies*. Bride and groom were pleased with that but resisted an attempt to assign a Victorian scholar to their honeymoon. They had to run a gauntlet of arguments. "Lewis Carroll would have wanted it." (The Lewis Carroll pro tem said "Certainly not!") Their refusal was "like Thomas Moore agreeing to the burning of Byron's memoirs." "Inquiring academics want to know." But, in the end, these lovers fled into the night without benefit of scholarly scrutiny. "Just another frontal disturbance," said Hugh. "We've been through worse."

The honeymoon not only confirmed the prognosis of Compatibility IV but raised their sexual IQ significantly. The erotic glow which they took on during that short trip continued long after they had reimmersed themselves in things academic. It was still unabated when they attended a much publicized lecture entitled, "Phallocentrism in Ecclesiastical Architecture." Like most academic lectures, it did not start on time, and the young couple waited fifteen minutes with about two dozen others to "allow people time to arrive." Only two more did, and, after a forgettable introduction, the speaker made an unforgettable entrance from the wings. From a flowing, high-collared black gown emerged a ghostly-white long neck supporting a ghostly-white countenance. Only face powder in excess could have produced so unnatural a complexion. But the most striking feature was the hair—light grey frizzed out horizontally on all sides. Combined with the white face and neck and the long black gown, it gave the effect of a mushroom cloud rising out of a shroud, and the voice, when it came, was equally startling— a low, mournful monotone in cadence slow. "Bringing the eternal

The honeymoon… raised their sexual IQ significantly.

This growing phallocentrism suggested that religion needed male underpinning.

note of sadness in," thought Hugh. It was like a voice from a cave.

And indeed it was of caves she began to speak, of those early places of worship—the Altamira Cave, the catacombs—her list seemed inexhaustible. The thing to be noted was that early humans worshipped in feminine space, whether in womb-like caves or above upon the round womb of the earth. That is why in early times religion was fertile and life-enhancing. She moved on to Norman architecture with its massive pillars. This growing phallocentrism suggested that religion needed male underpinning. The rounded interior of the cave had been rectangularized, and the church interior had taken on a decidedly unfeminine look except for the rounded arches between columns which preserved a vaginal balance against the growing phallocentrism. There remained, of course, the concave baptismal font, but it was often imprisoned behind iron bars, an ominous foreshadowing of the phallocentrist tyranny to come.

"And...come...it...did." The speaker became self-consciously dramatic before falling back into her monotone. Phallocentrism reached its zenith in the Gothic style, with phallic images everywhere, not only in the slender pillars. The openings between pillars, vaginal in the Norman style, had been perverted into narrower pointed (phallic) arches. The windows too had become narrow, pointed and phallic, foreshadowing the interballistic missiles in which the link has become apparent between phallocentric religion and the destruction of war.

The speaker now had turned to the modern world, which has been misnamed "secular." Our world has returned, she said, to the worship of early gods without recognizing them as gods—

not to life-enhancing matriarchal divinities, but to Mammon, who is worshipped in the phallic skyscrapers of every big city, and to Mars, whose spirit is enshrined in every phallic missile silo. She called for a "return to the womb," to the salvific power of woman, and again deviated from her monotone in a dramatic close: "There can be no Peacekeeper in a missile silo; the natural tendency of an erect phallus is to ejaculate!"

It was a startling conclusion. The mushroom cloud above the black shroud stood before them as the ghost of Hiroshimas yet to come. The audience sat entranced before this oracle of some forgotten goddess, except for Professor Cutter, a logic-machine of the first order whose sympathetic imagination would rate at best a one on a scale of ten. He had a question regarding the cathedrals with their phallic underpinnings of columns, whether Norman or Gothic. Had not these cathedrals also underpinnings of walls? And were not those walls symbolically hymens? Were not those phallic pillars shut up in the womb as it were, woman still dominant?

It was a trance-shattering question, but in the mushroom cloud Professor Cutter had met his match. Indeed the ecclesiastical walls are hymens, she agreed. Professor Cutter was to be congratulated on having seen that. Would he had seen farther! Each wall had a door, an opening through which people were constantly entering. Such sexual penetration was "a ritual enactment of male rape fantasies." The follow-up questions were predictable enough. If entering a church was sexual penetration, was not sexual intercourse equivalent to entering a church? If religion was sexual in nature, was not intercourse religious in nature, and therefore was the speaker not

It was a trance-shattering question, but in the mushroom cloud Professor Cutter had met his match.

Theirs was a laughing love — the richest kind.

saying the same thing as John Donne in "The Canonization"? The discussion reached its nadir when someone asked if leaving church before the end of the service was "premature withdrawal." Alice and Hugh chose that moment to leave. An evening that had momentarily transcended the academic had become bogged down in it.

When Alice and Hugh made love that night it was with a raised consciousness of the relationship of sex and the sacred. "May I enter your holy of holies?" he asked.

"If you promise not to genuflect." Theirs was a laughing love — the richest kind. "You're a pattern for lovers, Hugh. John Donne could not have been better."

"You would bring out the best in any lover."

"Donne would have wanted More."

"More would have been less."

"Donne has been outdone once more."

The rest was ecstasy.

Other Stories

A Very Fishy Story

A Very Fishy Story

> *"We move forward at near the speed of light...our brilliance is never seen by those in other institutions who are regressing at nearly the same rate."*

To have brought together the two partners in some great enterprise—to have introduced Sir Arthur Sullivan to William S. Gilbert or Bud Abbott to Lou Costello—how great a satisfaction is to be found in that, whether history takes note of it or not. This story concerns a fortuitous introduction, the impact of which is soon to be felt by two great American institutions.

For many years I have sustained a friendship with Lucien Acuto, Professor of English at Cutting Edge College—an institution whose low visibility belies its scholarly advances. "We move forward at near the speed of light," Lucien likes to say, "so that our brilliance is never seen by those in other institutions who are regressing at nearly the same rate." It's his little joke, of course, but perhaps a truth in hyperbole. "Others may exhaust themselves struggling against the tide," he boasts. "My downstream strokes keep me ahead of the current."

Lucien will admit to having had his fling with tradition. Upon the bookcases in his impressive office rest busts of Aristotle, Descartes, Coleridge, and Samuel Johnson. (Thomas Rymer was put away quietly at a garage sale.) These busts, he has promised, will be mine when he is able to replace them with Saussure, Derrida, Barthes, and Stanley Fish. When such busts become available, Lucien intends to buy several of each—one set for his bookcases and the

...he used to lay claim to being "a reincarnation of Odysseus— the man never at a loss."

others as investments. They will escalate in value, he assures me, like old baseball cards and early comic books. Lucien is, of course, in the forefront of contemporary literary theory and expects to build his scholarly reputation upon the solid foundation of deconstruction. "Should there be a canon, Professor Acuto?" It is a question that makes his day. "Yes," he replies, "I believe in many canons—loose canons." And he laughs pleasantly in unison with a few students who understand the joke.

Lucien has always been popular with students, even though he challenges them relentlessly. He is too personable and good-humored to be intimidating, and he enjoys his little victories over younger adversaries so much that his protégés serve willingly as sparring partners. Though he never boasts of his extensive publications, he glories in his keen wit and used to lay claim to being "a reincarnation of Odysseus—the man never at a loss."

The day came, however, when (alas!) Lucien found himself completely at a loss. He and his class had spent the first half of a semester examining Renaissance poetry in the light of Stanley Fish's reader-response theory. "It is an illusion," Lucien proclaimed, "that the text speaks to you. There is, in fact, no text in the sense of a meaningful utterance. There is only a linguistic pattern upon which you, the readers, confer meaning." (He was delighted when one of his students deconstructed the word *conference* into *conférence*.) All went well, class after class (meaning-full conférence after meaning-full conférence) and Lucien actually looked forward to reading the midterm exams. But the results were disappointing. Several of the brighter students had written rather intelligent essays, but had badly misread the questions. Curiously, all offered the same defense: "But, professor, your questions have no inherent meanings. They have only the meanings that the interpreting community creates for them." The interpreting community, they pointed out, could only be the students, since to include the professor would be to fall into the intentional fallacy. Lucien smelled a conspiracy but found himself without an adequate listener response. What would Odysseus do now? Lucien was at a loss, but his love of wit saved him from dejection. He who gloried in outwitting students felt his heart beating with applause. He readily conceded their point when they suggested to him that written examinations are based on a predeconstruction construct that is now exploded. Examinations should be abolished. Lucien agreed to take their suggestion under advisement.

A rereading of the examination papers was enlightening. A disparity, however great, between the intended meaning of a question and the perceived meaning seemed not to undermine the quality of the answer; it may have enhanced the quality, Lucien theorized. There was just one "essay," which he found quite unacceptable, and he so informed the student. This young woman had remembered Robert Frost's response to a question about one of his poems: "It means what it means to you." She had proceeded to exploit the doctrine of the transmigration of souls in a piece of doggerel — old-fashioned, end-stopped quatrains with predictable rhymes — climaxing in the line "Stanley Fish is Robert Frost." Lucien told her that (a) her poem was conspicuously derivative of a poem about the Battle of Trafalgar with its startling "Nelson was Francis Drake" and (b) that, since Stanley Fish had been born before Robert Frost died, her poem assumed

"What would Odysseus do now?"

There are arguments to which no response is possible...

the impossible. She replied (a) that all of Shakespeare's plays are derivative and (b) that the transmigration of souls, as she envisions it, is analogous to a relay race — as the baton is passed it always remains for a time in the hands of both the runner who is finishing and the one who is to continue in his place. There are arguments to which no response is possible, and Lucien knew that he had just heard one.

Adept as he was in deconstructing poetry, my learned friend realized that "to strive, to seek, to find" sometimes involves "to yield." In Lucien's classes examinations have now gone the way of the old New Criticism, and he is proud that his students were the first to see them as anachronistic. Lucien's current course on Nineteenth-Century-Women Poets is a cooperative enterprise, in which professor and students beget meaning upon the body of one poem after another without fear of being "found out" under subsequent questioning. All academia will be able to read about the Acuto method in Lucien's forthcoming book *Promiscuous Co-creation*. The title is a compromise with his publisher, who thought that *I Pimp for Christina Rossetti* would have more marketability.

At this point, I must leave Lucien Acuto, and travel south and west to Lackaday — a sleepy town on the cutting edge of nothing, which would be enjoying total obscurity were it not the home of a minor league baseball team whose scores are dutifully reported in the metropolis of the parent team. That near-obscurity is about to be brightened by a national spotlight, and here's how it all began.

The Lackaday Tumblers play at a level of professional ball that is a training ground for the rawest and most questionable talent, not only of players but of umpires. Occasionally — not often — a player at this level achieves a meteoric rise to national fame, but for umpires the climb has always been at the pace of an inchworm. Now it seems that a relatively inexperienced umpire, Miro Dentro, is on the verge of celebrity status; so too is a minor league announcer, Mike Sounder, who happens to be my friend and who has provided me with a play-by-play of what is destined to be a historic moment in sports.

On that soon-to-be-famous day, a suspicious Lackaday batter asked to see the ball he had just missed, and showed the soon-to-be-famous umpire what was clearly a scuff mark. The Lackaday manager predictably rushed out and demanded that the opposition pitcher be ejected for throwing a "doctored" ball. Dentro was not, as they say, cut from the same cloth as his fellows, having completed all course work for a degree in linguistics before leaving his tree-shaded campus for the sunbaked diamonds of the most minor of minor leagues. Dentro acknowledged that the ball held by the Lackaday batter was indeed scuffed, but held that it did not follow that he had swung at a scuffed ball. He explained with great patience some of the current linguistic theory.

"Linguistic utterances are made up of irreducible atoms called 'phonemes,' distinguished by the presence or absence of certain immanent features. The presence of such a feature is called a 'mark.' For example /s/ (as in sat) is distinguished from /z/ (as in zoom) in that the latter is voiced whereas the former is generally unvoiced. This voicing is a 'mark.' But context can cause an /s/ to become marked, as when it falls between vowels (as in *easy*). And though /z/ is marked by voicing in an English context, it loses that mark in a Spanish context (as in *zapata*)." The Lackaday manager had the

Linguistic utterances are made up of irreducible atoms called 'phonemes'

"A pitch upon which the interpreting community might confer curvature."

look of a man trying to see the bottom of a ten-fathom lake with a half-fathom of visibility. Dentro then made his analogy. "That ball, stationary in the hand, clearly bears a scuff mark. But a mark, by definition, is an *observable* characteristic. When a ball leaves the pitcher's hand, it is traveling between seventy-five and ninety-five miles per hour. In that context, there is no observable mark and hence, by definition, the ball is *un*marked. The batter always swings at an unmarked ball."

Dentro's decision took on the status of a legal precedent around the league, as did subsequent decisions based upon linguistic analogies. My announcer friend, Mike, was telling me how Dentro is bringing about a grass roots revolution in baseball — a revolution that, like all revolutions, requires many adjustments. It will not do anymore for an enlightened announcer to say "curve ball" — he must say "a pitch upon which the interpreting community might confer curvature." The pace of announcing has slowed considerably, but that is to the good since a baseball game consists mostly of pauses during which the announcer can be hard put to find something to say. Other changes are occurring at this minor league level. Some umpires and managers are planning to take linguistics courses in the off-season. Advertisements for books on structuralism and deconstruction have begun to appear in baseball programs. Linguistic delays have begun to rival rain delays in duration, though, as in the past, a linguistic delay can undergo a sudden "transformation" into that non-linguistic interaction which the interpreting community labels a "donnybrook" — a context in which some players unmarked in most contexts become marked.

I have just recently introduced Mike Sounder to Lucien, and wheels are turning like blender blades. Mike told of that soon-to-be-famous day in Lackaday and explained how linguistics was making inroads into baseball. "Already some managers are learning how to deconstruct the rule book. Umpire training will have to include courses in linguistics. Veteran umpires will require retraining." Lucien, knowing that time has a way of deconstructing opportunity, was on the phone before Mike had finished, urging the president of Cutting Edge to offer a ten-year contract to an a.b.d. umpire in Lackaday "before the competition grabs him up!" A proposal has since been swiftly but quietly making its way through the academic bureaucracy for a graduate program in linguistics with a concentration in baseball, for which Mike Sounder is to be director of admissions and recruiting.

My part in all this has been a small one; the marriage of baseball and linguistics would eventually have taken place without me. But in bringing together Lucien and my announcer friend, I had, for however brief a time, my foot on the accelerator of history. And what constructive developments are to be expected! Linguistic theory and textual analysis will no longer be seen as academic exercises without practical application, and baseball—long considered lowbrow entertainment—is about to find a place in the intellectual life of America.

"Already some managers are learning how to deconstruct the rule book."

Narrative Epistolary:
Novice Poet Quite Unwary,
Referee A Bit Contrary

Narrative Epistolary: Novice Poet Quite Unwary, Referee A Bit Contrary

The following letter arrived with the required SASE:

Editor
Journal of Non-Textuality

Dear Editor,

I am submitting for possible publication in the Journal of Non-Textuality the enclosed poem. It may not be the sort of thing you're looking for—perhaps not non-textual enough. Should you find it unsuitable for your journal, would you please send some words of encouragement.

Yours truly,

Newman Hopewell
Hillside Hollow Community College

To which was attached:

Meditations of a Muddling Mender

Some minds there are that do not love a text,
That want it gone, that send the swollen theory
Under it and make gaps even logic can
Not mend. There on the page they do not need
A text; such god-like theorists create
Ex nihilo a mental construct free
Of all restraint, whether of text or author's
Known intent. The deconstructionists
Are another case, exposers of
An intratextine war where meanings fall
As victims all foredoomed. These practiced lazer
Eyes would leave no doubt (except among
Naive traditionalists) linguistic clothes,
However elegant, do yet enfold
No emperor.

Such critic-theorists
Work not alone but schedule interchange
And on the days appointed meet to share
Textual erasures, insights bold,
Visions and revisions, rich cuisine,
And self-consuming nightlife well deserved.

Oh, just another kind of indoor game.
It comes to little more. The world goes on
Without them (this they know), but it's a dreamer-
Peopled world (this too they know), a land
Of fog where language-bound the masses grope,
Where in imagined meanings lesser lights
May find imagined bliss, where, if such meanings
Deconstruct unprompted, simple souls
Will muddle through, until from ashes shall
New hope arise to brighten up the fog.
Our prophet-theorists above the mist
Share cabalistic wisdom hard to grasp
And find their keys to bliss in proverbs new:
Neither a muddler nor a mender be;
Keep meanings hidden and thyself on view.

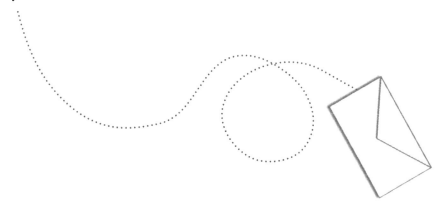

To which a kindly editor made reply:

Dear Newman Hopewell,

We regret that we are unable to use your poem in the *Journal of Non-Textuality*. One of our referees wrote the following critique, which I am pleased to pass along.

This "poet" has labored under the influence (as Harold Bloom would say) without ever emerging as a free creative spirit. In his choice of blank verse he places himself in the tradition of serious meditative poetry—a placement reinforced by the ubiquitous Frostian echoes. His anxiety of influence is betrayed by the subtext of a Popean satirical tone, quite at odds with the meditative tradition. The poem is thus hopelessly at odds with itself. From the ashes of this self-consuming artifact, no phoenix shall arise.

I hope you will find the above critique helpful and that, in revised form, your poem will find an outlet in a less selective journal.

Best wishes,

Barry R. Rief
Editor

To which Newman Hopewell did respond:

Dear Mr. Rief,

I thank you for forwarding a critique of my poem, though I cannot accept the judgment of the anonymous referee. It is a double disappointment when rejection is accompanied by an invalid reason. I do not deny writing under the influence, but find it enhances my literary efforts.

As my wife puts it, "Newman's creative energies are bottled in the Napa Valley." Edgar Allen Poe composed beautifully under the influence, as did Samuel Taylor Coleridge. If I am following such illustrious predecessors in my modus operandi, what cause is there for anxiety? A jug of wine, a goblet, and blank paper here before me in my study—that has ever been my most creative context.

But thanks for your encouragement. I shall revise my poem and seek a less selective journal. Tomorrow to fresh words and outlets new!

Gratefully yours,

Newman Hopewell

To which letter there was no response.

The Last
Shall Be First:
Dr. Valyu
beneath the
founder's
portrait

The Last Shall Be First

The students and graduates seemed innoculated against the flippancy and macabre humor celebrated in M.A.S.H. and The Doctor.

Eighty years after its establishment, the Last School of Medicine still had the glow of youth. Founder and first president I. B. Last had prophesied its immortality (and consequently his own) to benefactors who, though they believed in his abilities, thought his prophecies a bit extreme. He graciously accepted their doubts along with their money, and his prophecy gained credibility as the years passed, thanks to the zeal of that faith community known as the Last Alumni Association. Dr. Last had impressed upon generations of medical students that they, as well as the institution, were his immortality. "I live on in you!" He proclaimed it at assemblies and whispered it in each casual contact. Succeeding presidents relayed that message so movingly that by graduation day each young physician could feel the lifeblood of the founder pulsing through his or her veins. And so, shortly after the Founder's death, at the urging of the Alumni Board of Governors, the Development Office ordered inscribed on their letterhead the legend "We are Last."

This transfer of lifeblood could not have taken hold more firmly had it been biological. Students and graduates seemed innoculated against the flippancy and macabre humor celebrated in *M.A.S.H.* and *The Doctor*. The phenomenon had been discussed at some length by a psychiatrist graduate in an article entitled "Spiritual Genetics." Whatever other factors might be involved, some of the

Dr. Valyu is always a good draw, being that rarity of rarities, a late twentieth-century Renaissance man.

credit must go to the artist whose oversized portrait of Dr. Last occupies the center third of the wall above the lectern in Founder's Hall. The kindness shown in the mouth is upstaged completely by the soul-baring penetration of the most intense eyes ever committed to canvas. Under this intimidating gaze were announced some of the most important breakthroughs in the science of medicine. But no speaker could compete for attention with the eyes of Dr. Last until Dr. D. Valyu, just one week ago, delivered his startling address on "The Impossibility of Medicine." The lecture hall had filled up that night for the first time in anyone's memory. Dr. Valyu is always a good draw, being that rarity of rarities, a late twentieth-century Renaissance man. He had served as a male midwife, one might say, at the rebirth of skepticism, and so relished his reputation as a master iconoclast that he was offended at being characterized "the Mencken of Medicine." Inadequate praise is harder to deal with than negative criticism.

"The Impossibility of Medicine"?!? An impossible title. Whatever could it mean? Medicine was the Founder's great cause. Medicine was the mission of the school and of every graduate. Some physicians were beginning to think that all things were possible with medicine, or soon would be. So Valyu's title had a perverse attraction for students, faculty, and administrators alike. They crowded into the great hall until every seat had been taken and every aisle was filled with squatters contemptuous of the fire code.

The speaker could have made a tardy and therefore more dramatic entrance, but every iconoclast has his own idols, and Dr. Valyu worshipped punctuality. Promptly at the appointed hour of eight, the eminent man stepped behind the lectern and gave his impossible thesis an irrefutable argument.

It did not surprise his listeners when the speaker began discussing literary theory. The opening of a Valyu lecture seldom gave a clue to where it was headed. He spoke first of the Shakespearean criticism of Samuel Taylor Coleridge, of how Coleridge found in the plays a subtle organic unity akin to that found in the plant and animal kingdoms. Such unity, thought Coleridge, was far more natural than, and therefore superior to, that achieved by the observation of the classical unities or by following the conventions of the epic or the pastoral elegy. Dr. Valyu then jumped ahead ("if I may be allowed a *saltus*") to the deconstructionist rejection of organic unity in literary works. He spoke of how linguistic analysis had found language to be a closed system of arbitrary signs which always, under close scrutiny, collapse into a jumble of contradictions. "It is on *this basis* [emphasis Dr. Valyu's] that the deconstructionists claim to have discredited organic unity as a literary theory. *But* [emphasis again Dr Valyu's], as so often happens, they were right for the wrong reason. Organic unity is impossible in literature [crescendo followed by dramatic pause] because [second dramatic pause] it does not exist in biology [murmurs in the audience]."

Dr. D. Valyu raised his hand for silence, his eyes sparkling in anticipation of a triumph. The audience was hooked. Should he play with them a while or begin to reel them in? He opted for the latter. "Organic unity in nature is an illusion—a fiction, as Wallace Stevens might say [murmurs of 'who?']. If I may reverse the Coleridgean analogy, just as a poem is a 'self-consuming artifact,' so is the human

Promptly at the appointed hour of eight, the eminent man stepped behind the lectern and gave his impossible thesis an irrefutable argument.

"...just as a poem is a 'self-consuming artifact,' so is the body a self-consuming naturefact..."

body a self-consuming naturefact [pause in pride of the coinage]not because its unity will one day be undone by death, but because that unity never existed. The body is as hopelessly at odds with itself as any literary text. A mechanism for swallowing coexists with a mechanism for vomiting [Dr. Valyu was speeding up his delivery]; the intake of water is negated by perspiration and urination; the veins continually undo the work of the arteries." D. Valyu moved through his catalogue like a pinball bumping its way toward a record score. It seemed to the listeners that the piercing eyes in the Founder's portrait flashed with each hit. By the time the speaker paused, he was looming larger behind the lectern, and the portrait seemed to have shrunk. "Thus," intoned Valyu, "the organic unity of the body is illogical and consequently impossible. The inescapable conclusion is that the science of medicine, an attempt to sustain and restore such unity, has... no...validity." Valyu looked intently from one member of the audience to another, tacitly inviting a challenge. There was none, and no wonder. To reject the argument was to reject logic itself. Valyu saw the anxiety of affluence setting in. He saw looks of desperation, looks that pleaded "Don't leave us here." And, because the speaker was a kindly man, he did not.

"What then are physicians to do? [dramatic pause] We must cease to practice our now exploded profession and turn to educating fellow humans on their chaotic physical state. It will be an easy adjustment for them. Patients are always relieved to hear that their condition is natural. But it will not be an easy adjustment for us. It will require much humility to admit that the humanities have outstripped—nay, dethroned—science in the pursuit of truth and to admit finally what the avant garde in literary theory has well established: it is not reality that is the test of theory but theory that is the test of reality."

D. Valyu again surveyed his audience. The worried looks remained. He went on. "What will be most difficult for physicians is to overcome their fear that, in an age of deconstruction biology, their incomes will decline. Fear not." The speaker then supplied startling statistics on the incomes of leading literary theorists and practitioners. The morale of his audience was rising steadily, as D. Valyu approached his reassuring close: "Those who think that a shift from constructive practice to deconstructive theory results in a lower income have still more to learn from the humanities."

The speaker looked out now upon faces relaxed and smiling. Then began the applause, spontaneous and unrestrained. Led by the current president, they rose to their feet with sustained enthusiasm and shouts of "Bravo!" So wild was their response that they were oblivious to the change in the countenance of the speaker. A smirk of satisfaction had given way to a growing anxiety. So loud was their response that they did not hear D. Valyu's cautionary "Check your calendars." Had it occurred to them that it was April first, it would not have mattered. Irrefutable logic must be respected any day of the year. Dr. Valyu had cast for a blowfish, and suddenly he was King Neptune wanting to abdicate. It was no use. They would have their king. He looked up at the Founder. Fainter was the smile on the lips, the light in the eyes — devalued, one might say.

Within a few days, the editor of the *Journal of the American Medical Dissociation* (JAMD) asked and secured permission to print

> *"What will be most difficult for physicians is to overcome their fear that, in an age of deconstruction biology, their incomes will decline."*

His ideas were spreading through the medical community in hospital lounges, on golf courses, and at cocktail parties.

"The Impossibility of Medicine" in that radical new publication, assuring widespread dissemination of this revolutionary breakthrough. But the immediate coverage was disappointing. A news conference was called for the day following the lecture. Dr. D. Valyu would reveal to the media his findings on the relationship between literary theory and anatomy. Only three reporters showed. Two of them took off before the conference began, having been ordered to the courthouse to cover an important jury verdict. There remained only a reporter from the *Tabloid Tattler*, who explained, "We wrote that story yesterday." So the only coverage for Dr. Valyu was in the *Tabloid Tattler*, the blurb on the cover page reading:

Physician uses logic to explode human body — thousands cheer!

Doctor Valyu read the *Tattler* account with a smile. No matter. His ideas were spreading through the medical community in hospital lounges, on golf courses, and at cocktail parties. His thoughts drifted to Plato's concept of the philosopher-king, still a rarity after more than two millennia. "At least we shall have the philosopher-physician," he mused. "It's a start."

Never-in-Print Titles

Never-in-Print Titles

(To Be Made Available On Demand)

Shadowing the Private Eye

Stan Lee Shark, textual investigator, famed for solving cases of his own creation, has settled into his Southern mansion, only to find that his library is haunted by ghosts of meanings past. A team of ghostbusters, wearing the blue of Derrida, Inc., conduct an extermination that is as effective as it is endless.

Oedipus Scriptor: If Words Could Kill

Fame was the spur, a phallic pen the patricidic murder weapon. But who was the victim? And was he dead before the fatal thrust? A thrilling excursion into the influential world of Bloomtown anxiety.

Life and Loves of a She-Critic

Stella Orbis, interstellar traveller of the literary firmament, discovers that a time warp has been responsible for the traditional canon. Join Stella for her critical voyage on which "bluestockings" swell into red giants and presumed luminosities, deprived of the brightness gained by proximity, collapse into white dwarves.

The Reader as Sancho

Bookie Climber, poring over learned journals, fell asleep and dreamt he was eating sawdust. Like Keats's Adam, with the scholarly prose still before him, "he awoke and found it truth." Something had to be done. Set out with this modern Quixote on his impossible dream of bringing style to academic discourse.

Margaret Walker contributes her extensive background in print advertising design, copywriting and marketing to construct Joe Wessling's Alice In Academe. *A cowgirl at heart who loves open spaces (and waters), she is pursuing a career in interior space planning.*

Photo by Robert K. Ander